366 and more
ANIMAL FABLES

*Translated from the Italian and
re-told by Maureen Spurgeon*

Brown Watson
ENGLAND

The Three Little Pigs

THERE were once three little pigs who decided to go out into the world to seek their fortune. The first thing each of them wanted was a house!

The first little pig walked and walked – until he met a man with a load of straw on his back.

"Good man," said the little pig, "will you give me some straw to build a house?"

So the man gave the pig some straw, and very soon the house was built. But the little pig had only just sat down in his new home, when – KNOCK-KNOCK-KNOCK! – there was somebody at the door!

"Little pig!" came a voice. It sounded quite gentle, but the pig knew it was the wolf! "Little pig! Let me come in!"

"No, no!" cried the little pig. "By the hair of your chinny-chin-chin, I will NOT let you in!"

"Then," roared the wolf, "I'll huff, and I'll puff, and BLOW your house in!" So he huffed and he puffed and blew at the house of straw, until it flew away like a dry, autumn leaf.

The first little pig just managed to escape and ran away as fast as he could!

And the second little pig? He had met a man carrying a load of wood on his back.

"Good man," said the second little pig. "Will you give me some wood? I want to build myself a little house!"

So the man handed over some wood, and the second little pig began work. He had just finished building his little house, when up came the first little pig, panting hard.

"Th-the wolf is coming after me!" He gasped for breath. "He huffed and he puffed and blew away my house of straw!" "Come into my little house of wood," said the second little pig, "and bolt the door!" But before long, they heard KNOCK-KNOCK-KNOCK – and the voice of the wolf. "Little pig! Let me come in!"

"No, no!" cried the second little pig. "By the hair of your chinny-chin-chin, I will NOT let you in!"

"No?" howled the wolf.

"Then I'll huff, and I'll puff, and BLOW your house in!" So he huffed and he puffed and blew the house of wood up into the air like a feather.

The two little pigs just managed to run away before the wolf could catch them!

Meanwhile, the third little pig had met a man pushing a barrow loaded with bricks.

"Good man," said the little pig, "may I please have some bricks to build a house?"

So, the man gave him some bricks.

The third little pig began work, laying bricks carefully and making his house safe and strong. He had nearly finished when his two brothers came running. "The wolf is after us!" they panted. "He huffed and he puffed and he blew down our house of wood!"

"Help me finish," said the third little pig, "then we can all go inside my house!" The house of bricks was only just finished, when the little pigs heard KNOCK-KNOCK-KNOCK! at the door!

"Little pig!" cried the wolf. "Little pig! Let me come in!"

"No, no!" cried the third little pig. "By the hair of your chinny-chin-chin, I will NOT let you in!"

The wolf gave a great howl. "Then I'll huff, and I'll puff, and BLOW your house in!"

So he huffed and he puffed. Then he puffed. And he huffed. But the house did not even move! The wolf could hear the three little pigs dancing for joy, and he was furious! And he was hungry! Then he had an idea. He climbed to the top of the house and tried to get down the chimney. He did not know that the three little pigs had lit a fire and set a big pot of stew to cook!

Before he knew what was happening, the wolf had fallen headlong into the cooking pot! With the lid slammed down and the water beginning to boil – the wolf ended up like a pink sausage! Those three little pigs were safe at last!

January

1 The Billy who wanted to be a Mountain Goat

Melegari

Little Billy Goat was tired of being part of a herd and following the orders of the goatherd. So, he ran away to join the mountain goats who lived as they pleased among the rocks and ravines.

The mountain goats welcomed Billy and he soon made friends. Then, one fine day, the youngest felt their horns beginning to sprout. Billy Goat's horns began to grow, too! But, whilst his horns grew slowly, those of the mountain goats grew and grew, looking very grand, indeed!

When the mountain goats started teasing him about it, Billy felt very unhappy and so alone. There was no other goat like him who could help to cheer him up and make him see that everyone has something of which they can be proud. At last, frightened of being left on his own, Billy went home and joined the herd once more. He never wanted to be like a mountain goat again.

2 The Dog and the Meat

Aesop

One day, a dog was passing by the door of a house where an enormous piece of meat, as thick as the trunk of a small tree, lay on a plate.

"Hey!" he thought to himself. "What a feed that would make!" Very quickly, he went inside, jumped up and grabbed the meat in his mouth. Then he ran and ran, until he came to a grassy bank, where a stream flowed bright and clear.

"Now for a good meal!" thought the dog. "And a cool drink, too!"

But – as he went to put his paw in the water, he could see another dog! A dog with an ENORMOUS piece of meat in its mouth, as big as the one he had!

He opened his mouth and went to bite the other dog's meat – and the meat he had been holding fell into the stream and was carried out of sight: which just goes to show that we should not risk losing what we have for the sake of dreams.

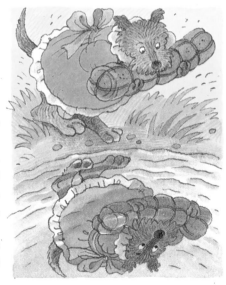

3 The Wolf, the Lioness and the Mule

Regnier

A wolf and a lioness were each prowling around the forest, feeling very hungry. "I'm finished!" howled the wolf at last. He closed his eyes and lay on the ground.

How long he stayed there, the wolf never knew. Then – something made him open his eyes. And there, between him and the lioness, he saw a lovely, plump mule, nibbling the grass.

"Saved!" thought the wolf. "We'll get that mule between us, the lioness and me!" He winked at the lioness, and she winked back. Together, they advanced towards the mule.

What a silly creature she looked, thought the wolf! Why, she wasn't even running away! "Who are you?" he asked. "Where do you come from?"

"I don't know," said the mule, her mouth full of green grass. "My mother says I'm too stupid to learn my own name! So I've written it under my foot! Would you like to see?" And the mule lifted a hind leg.

"I'm sorry..." said the wolf, "I cannot see clearly...."

"Let me look!" roared the lioness, pushing past him.

Then the mule gave such a mighty kick on the head of the lioness, that she was knocked senseless!

And by the time the mule had lifted her hoof again, ready to hit the wolf, he was a long way off, his tummy as empty as a drum – and feeling very stupid and sorry for himself.

4 The Stag at the Pool

Aesop

As a stag drank at a pool, he studied his reflection in the water. He admired his antlers. But – how thin his legs were!

Hearing a pack of hounds, the stag ran to the woods. He caught his antlers in some low branches, pulling himself free just in time. And as those thin, spindly legs carried him away from danger, he quite forgot how much he had admired those beautiful antlers!

5 The Fox and the Goslings

from France

One day, Mr. Fox came across a family of goslings. "Hah!" he cried. "Some feast you'll make!" "Please," said the biggest gosling, "let us each say a last prayer!" And at once he began, "Qua! Qua! Qua! Qua! - - -" Then another gosling began. "Qua! Qua! Qua! Qua - - -" Then a third, a fourth, a fifth – and by the time they had all finished, Fox was already halfway home with a headache!

6 The Little Monkey and the Puppy

Clasio

There was once a little monkey who lived in a house, along with a man and his puppy dog. One evening, the man went out, leaving the little monkey and the puppy by themselves. When the time came to go to bed, the monkey picked up the candle, as the man always did.

"No!" barked the puppy. "Please, do not leave me alone in the dark!"

"Step back a moment!" smiled the monkey. "Look over your shoulder, and you'll see another candle, burning just behind you!" (It was a reflection of the candle in a mirror!) "Well," said the monkey, "do you see it?"

"Yes!" said the puppy. "I do see it, but –" Before he finished speaking, the monkey blew out the candle, and he found himself alone in the dark!

And that was when he learned that things are not always what they seem.

7 The Sparrow who was too careful

Florian

One day, a cat put his paw in water, then a bag of corn. So, his paw was covered with grain.

Stretched out in the grass, this paw looked like an ear of corn. And as sparrows came and pecked at the corn – so they ended up in the cat's mouth!

One sparrow thought every ear of corn was a cat's paw. Too afraid to eat anything, he went back to his nest, hungry.

8 The Horse and the Ass

Aesop

A horse and an ass were going along, the ass weighed down by a great load. "Please," he said to the horse, "will you help me? You have little to carry!"

The horse just tossed its proud head. Seeing this, their master took the heavy things off the back of the ass and loaded them on to the horse. How the horse wished then he had agreed to help the ass, sharing the load between them.

9 The Two Sardines

Melegari

There were once two sardines who lived happily enough, swimming about in the sea. The first sardine was all blue and silver, like the rest of his family. But he wanted to be pink, with black spots on his back, with a gold tummy and tail. "I wish I could look different!" he told the second sardine.

"How can you do that?" asked the second sardine. He thought his friend looked fine exactly as he was.

"Easy!" said the first sardine – who was not as clever as the second sardine. And for a while he looked longingly at other fish, wishing he could be like them… The handsome, strong-swimming salmon, splashed with bright streaks of gold… The lively trout, black on top, white underneath with rainbow stripes on its sides….

Even when the two sardines found themselves in a fishing net, the first sardine was still moaning. "Wish I had whiskers like a mullet! Or I wouldn't mind being black and white, like a mackerel…"

"Be quiet!" cried the second sardine. "Fancy talking like that now!" The first sardine did not answer. He had already lost his head, ready to be cooked and tinned. The second sardine wriggled free. He used his head for things which really mattered – instead of wasting it on things which could never come true.

10 The Silly Young Cockerel

Melegari

There was once a young cockerel who thought he could guard the king. "I'll go right away and see him!" he decided.

He asked Mother Fox the way, and she led him to a hole in the ground. "Go in!" she said. "This is where the king lives!"

That silly, young cockerel! It was the foxes' lair, with Mr. Fox waiting to pounce – and thinking what a fine meal the cockerel would make!

11 The Fox and the Mask

Fedro

A fox came to a woodland picnic area, littered with cartons, milk bottles and plastic bags. "Ignorant people!" the fox thought. He stopped. And he looked again. "One of them," he muttered, "has even left behind his own head!"

For, there among the grass was a human face, looking up at him with such a solemn expression!

"Hello…" began the fox. There was no answer. "Excuse me, but – how did you lose your head?" Still no answer. The fox began to get angry. He bent down to sniff at the face – and it was then he found that the "person" was no more than a party mask!

"How nice!" he murmured. Then, making sure that there was nothing behind the mask added, "Nice – but quite empty! Yet these humans go around thinking they've got such fine brains!"

12 The Monkey and the Peas

Tolstoy

Want to test your patience? Try carrying peas with your hands cupped together! That's what one monkey did, with lots of peas to carry! When he dropped a pea, he went to pick it up – and dropped another twenty! He gave a sigh – and dropped the rest! So, he had to bend down and pick up the peas, one by one. THEN he found out how much patience he really did have!

13 The Lion and the Onager

Aesop

The onager is the wild ass of Asia, quite a fierce animal and a favourite target for hunters. And the onager in this story wanted to be friends with the lion.

"I'm a good hunter!" said the onager. "Just watch, and –"

"All right!" interrupted the lion, and crouched down on the ground.

Well, the onager caught a gazelle, a zebra, and a gnu (which is like a big ox, with a hump) and brought them back to the lion.

"My prey is shared out in turn!" roared the lion. "First share is mine, because I am king of the animals! Second share comes to me, so that I can divide everything equally! And I take the third share – because, if you DARE touch it, I shall eat you, too!"

And so the onager fled, thinking how it was that power always goes to those who are strongest.

14 The Blue-Tinted Jackal

from India

None of the jungle animals liked the jackal – because, instead of hunting for food, he would steal from others.

One day, prowling around, he fell into a tub of blue dye and crawled out the colour of a summer sky! And that gave him an idea....

He would say that he was a jackal coloured blue by a goddess as a sign that he was king of the animals!

Some animals believed him and built him a throne. Others waited for nightfall. Then they crept towards the throne where the jackal was sleeping and began making a noise. This woke the jackal, and without thinking, he cried out. Then all the animals knew who the blue jackal really was!

"What lies you've told us about being king!" they all shouted at him. But – the blue jackal was already making his escape!

15 The Elephant, the Hare and the Hippopotamus

from Africa

A hare was asked to lunch with the elephant, and to supper with the hippopotamus.

"Elephant," said the hare, "in seven days, you shall have a bunch of grass to eat, as big as a hippopotamus!"

To the hippopotamus, the hare promised, "In seven days, you shall have a bale of hay as fat as an elephant!"

When the seven days were up, the hare appeared with a long rope and tied one end to the elephant's trunk. "Pull!" said the hare. "Your bunch of grass is at the other end!"

Then the hare went to the hippopotamus, tying the other end of the rope to its tooth. "Pull!" cried the hare. "Your hay is at the other end!"

So the elephant and the hippopotamus pulled – and found themselves facing each other! That bad hare! Of course, they paid him back – but that is another story!

16 The Duck-Billed Platypus and the Lion

Melegari

Every so often, the lion would look around the animal kingdom, making sure everyone knew he was the most important!

"Look at you!" he sneered at the duck-billed platypus. "Your mouth is like the beak of a duck, which is a bird! Yet you have a skin like a dog – and four feet with fingers and toes like a human! Your young hatch from eggs like chickens, but suck milk like bear cubs!"

"Maybe you think you will soon roar like me!" the lion went on. "That would never do!"

And with a great roar, the lion knocked down the duck-billed platypus, long, pointed claws glinting in the sun.

But – the duck-billed platypus was no longer there! All the time the lion had been speaking, he had been busy, ready to make a quick getaway!

What the lion did not know was that the duck-billed platypus could also dig holes underground – just like a mole!

17 The Dog with a Bell

Fedro

There was once a dog who jumped up at people. So his master put a bell on his collar as a warning. "See this lovely bell my master bought me?" the dog kept saying. "That's because I'm such a fine dog!"

"Because you're such a nuisance, you mean!" one cheeky puppy answered.

People, too, can make the same thing appear something completely different.

18 The Fox and the Farmer

Aesop

A farmer was about to harvest his corn – when he saw a fox who had stolen some chickens, and captured him.

"Let me go!" cried the fox. "I swear I shall not go near your chickens again!"

"Your groans are more real than your promises!" roared the farmer.

"Calm down!" panted the fox, struggling furiously. "No need to flare up over nothing!"

"Flare up, do I?" roared the farmer. "We'll see about that!" He tied a bunch of straw to the tail of the fox, and set it alight!

In a panic, the fox pulled himself free. And as he ran through the field, all the corn caught fire! Before long, the farmer found himself without a single spear of corn!

And so this fable shows that everyone has to try to control their anger before that first strike of a match. Otherwise disaster will often follow, when all is lost.

19 The Bear and his coat

from Finland

Do you know why a bear has such a thick coat? Well, one story says this is because he was once a man who liked to climb trees!

But the trees he liked best had such sharp branches that they soon tore his clothes, and he was covered in scratches and grazes. So, the man prayed to Mother Nature, and she covered him in a thick, furry skin. The man had become a bear.

20 Little Mouse is Frightened

Trilussa

A mouse once crawled into a caravan which travelled many miles. One night, he came out to get a breath of fresh air – when a big, black shape loomed towards him.

"Who – who is it?" stammered the mouse.

"It is I!" came a great roar. "The lion!"

"Thank goodness!" sighed the mouse. "For one moment, I thought you were a cat!"

21 The Soldier and the Carob Tree

Melegari

The carob is a tree which grows in warm countries. It gets its name from the Arabic word *kharrubah* meaning "bean-pod" – because of the dark brown pods with beans inside which the tree produces.

Pods and beans can both be chewed, and it is believed that John the Baptist survived by eating carob whilst he was in the wilderness. One day, a soldier was slightly wounded in a battle. So, he rode his horse away for a little while, hoping to regain his strength. And as they stopped beneath a carob tree, the horse bit off one of the long pods. It tasted really good!

The soldier did the same, and very soon one was eating just as much as the other.

The horse and the soldier both enjoyed the peace, eating carob in the shady wood away from the battle.

Little by little, the soldier began feeling better. And once he felt his strength returning, he knew he was ready to take up the fight once again.

The horse, too, felt very refreshed. He began to trot, then to canter, then to gallop. And in a little while, they were back on the field of battle, fighting for victory!

After that, whenever the soldier needed energy, he and his horse always ate carob. Many people today follow the example of that soldier. Pods and beans are picked from the carob to make a type of chocolate.

22 The Swallow and the Cricket

Eveno

A man was listening to a grasshopper chirping, thinking what a lovely sound it was. Then, the noise stopped. The grasshopper had been caught by a swallow. "Oh, no!" cried the man. "How can you sing so beautifully, yet silence the song of another?"

But the swallow had already flown. Her chicks were waiting, and all she worried about was bringing them food.

23 The Cormorant and the Skua

from The Farne Islands

The Farne Islands lie in the Atlantic Ocean, off the coast of Denmark. Here, there lived a cormorant – a type of black sea raven – and a skua, which is a sea bird with thick, coloured feathers. Legend says that when birds came to choose their feathers, the cormorant wanted plumes with lots of colours. But the skua wanted the same.

At last, they agreed that the coloured feathers would go to the one who woke up the other to say that the sun had risen.

Night came. But only the skua went to sleep. The cormorant was determined to stay awake. And as the first glimmer of daylight appeared, he struggled to his feet. "It-it's day... " How weak he sounded! "It's day.. It's –" The cormorant could keep his eyes open no longer!

A little later, the first rays of the sun appeared. And from then on, the skua was dressed in beautiful, coloured feathers.

24 The Goat's Beard

Fedro

Billy Goat was very pleased when Mother Nature gave him a splendid beard. But when she also gave one to Nanny Goat, he didn't like it one bit!

"What does it matter?" Mother Nature said. "Beard or no beard, you will always be known for your bravery and strength!" This story tells us that we should be judged by our character, not our appearance.

25 Pinocchio and the Snake

Collodi

Pinocchio ran and ran down a little road, getting his wooden feet very muddy because it had been raining. He was hoping to find the fairy with the blue hair – but all at once, he came face to face with a snake as big as a tree, with great eyes of fire and its tail aflame.

"Excuse me…" Pinocchio began, "but can I get past?"

The snake hissed and stayed quite still, its tail smoking.

"It isn't moving at all…" Pinocchio thought. "Maybe it's dead…" He darted forward – but the snake rose up, eyes swirling, throwing itself so hard at Pinocchio that he was tossed into the air, turning three somersaults before he fell down again!

And as Pinocchio ran away, so the snake laughed and laughed, until – he went BANG! Then he really was dead.

Pride always comes before a fall.

26 The Frog and the Ox

Aesop

One day some frogs saw an ox for the first time. "What an animal!" sighed one.

"Quite enormous!" agreed another. "Makes us feel very small!" added a third.

"Pah!" burst out another frog. (He was a very conceited frog.) "YOU may all think you are smaller than him – but NOT me!"

He took a great, big gulp of air, swelling up until he was the size of a pear. "Was he THIS big?" he croaked.

"No!" cried the others. So the frog took gulp of air, puffing himself up until he was the size of a water-melon.

"Was he THIS big?" he croaked, holding his breath. "No!" came the answer. So the frog took another gulp of air, swelling bigger and bigger and bigger – until he exploded, with a deafening BANG!

It taught the other frogs that it is always silly to try to be like those we can never hope to become.

27 The Fish and the Cormorant

La Fontaine

A cormorant was getting old, and so could not catch enough fish to eat. So, he spread the news that a fisherman was coming and the fish were in danger! "I know a safe place to go!" he said. "Let me take you!" The fish agreed at once. And each one was carried in the beak of that cormorant to another pool with shallow water – and where he could eat them any time he liked.

28 The Sheep-Dog and the Oats

Melegari

Shep the sheep-dog had such long hair! It covered his eyes, his paws, and even grew right under his feet. Nobody knew how he could see sheep straying away from the flock, nor how he could reach them without tripping over himself.

One day, as Shep was guarding the sheep, he came across some wild oats.

"Don't touch us!" cried the stalks, lifting up their heavy ears. "Or you'll be sorry!"

"All right!" barked Shep. But, he sniffed at the oats – and as he went back to the flock, his face was covered in grain. He had touched the oats – now, war was declared!

To this day, the spears of oats and other grasses collect on the coats of long-haired dogs – which is why so many need to go to the vet to have them removed from their ears.

29 The Hen and the Wire-Worm

Melegari

A red wire-worm lay under the ground, her body curled seven times, as she had been taught. "Maybe," she thought after a while, "I need only curl up five times!" So, she uncurled a little. Then she uncurled herself again, and curled up four times, then three, then twice... Then she gave a lovely, big stretch, poked her head out and finished up in the beak of a farmyard hen!

30 The Fox, the Wolf and Good Manners

Clasio

One night, as a fox prowled around, he saw the cold eyes of the wolf, staring at him through the darkness.

"Going somewhere, Fox?" asked the wolf.

"I'm looking for a hen-house, full of chickens!" said the fox. "What about you?"

"Oh, I'm off to hunt for a lamb or two!" said the wolf.

"If you are on your best behaviour, you can come, too!"

"Thank you!" said the crafty old fox. "You're very kind!"

And, because he wanted to seem polite, he began walking a few paces behind the wolf, and to the left. The wolf was pleased.

"I'm glad to see you showing me some respect, Fox!" he said.

The fox and the wolf had gone some way, when they came to a prickly hedge. It had a narrow gap in the middle, through which they could pass, one at a time.

The wolf stopped, waiting to see what the fox would do.

The fox bowed very low. "After you, Wolf!" he said.

The wolf gave a smile and went through the hedge, his head held high with pride.

Next minute the fox heard a howl of pain. The wolf had been caught in a trap!

"Please help me!" he moaned. "My dear, good friend, Mr. Fox! Please help me get free!"

"You thought you should go first!" sneered the fox. "So you've got exactly what you wanted!"

And he went on his way.

31 The Animal Football Team

Melegari

The animal footballers were looking at their goal-nets. "I think they should be wider!" said the elephant. "What about a third goal-post in the middle?" cried Acrobats United – the apes' team. "No!" cried the giraffes. "Let's have them taller!"

"Lower!" squeaked the mice. None of the teams could agree. So, they had to leave the goals just as they were.

Pinocchio and the Parrot

ONE day, Pinocchio was given five pieces of gold to take home to Gepetto, his father! "What treasure this is!" he thought. "Now, Gepetto and I can live like gentlemen!"

But, he was not prepared for the cat and the fox. They pretended to be his friends – but all they really wanted was to steal Pinocchio's treasure.

First, the cat and the fox made Pinocchio spend one whole piece of gold buying them an enormous supper at The Red Crab Inn. Then Fox said, "Pinocchio, what will you do with your other four pieces of gold?"

"They're in my pocket," said Pinocchio proudly, "ready to take home to Gepetto!"

"Why not plant them in the Field of Miracles?" purred the fox. "That way, you will have a thousand gold pieces!"

"The Field of Miracles?" cried Pinocchio. "Is it far?"

"No!" said the fox. "You can walk there quite easily! Shall we show you where it is?" Pinocchio hesitated for just a moment. "Come on, then!" he said to the fox. "Let's go!"

They had to walk quite a way to a town with the odd name Fools' Paradise. Fox led the way through the streets, out of town and into a bare field.

"The Field of Miracles!" he declared. "Pinocchio, just dig a hole with your hands, put the gold pieces inside, then cover it over!" Pinocchio did as he was told.

"Now," continued the fox, "go over to that fountain get some water to dampen the soil!"

So Pinocchio went and filled one of his shoes with water.

"Is there anything else to do?" he asked, when he had watered the ground.

"No!" smiled the fox. "Come back in twenty minutes, and you will find a tree with branches weighed down with gold coins!"

And as he finished speaking, the fox and the cat waved goodbye and went on their way.

Pinocchio returned to town, counting the minutes until it was time to go back to The Field of Miracles.

"Supposing," he thought, "that instead of a thousand coins, I find TWO thousand on the tree? Or, FIVE thousand! Or, TEN thousand! Oh, I could build a palace with a thousand toys to play with, a cellar packed with lemonade and a library full of cakes and buns and sweets...!"

By now, Pinocchio was getting near the field, looking out for a tree with its branches weighed down by gold coins!

He could see nothing. The place where he had buried the coins was quite bare.

Suddenly, Pinocchio heard a loud laugh. He turned round sharply – and on a tree he saw a very big and very old parrot.

"What are you laughing at?" demanded Pinocchio.

"I'm laughing," chuckled the parrot, "because I tickled myself under my wing!"

"Huh!" scoffed Pinocchio. He went over to the fountain and filled one of his shoes with water. Then he came back and once more watered the ground where he had buried the gold pieces.

It was then he heard another laugh, much louder than before. "What a rude parrot you are!" cried Pinocchio angrily. "What are you laughing at this time?"

"I am laughing," chuckled the parrot, "at the fools who believe all the nonsense told to them by those more cunning than them!"

"Are you talking about me?" asked Pinocchio, after a pause.

"Yes I am!" squawked the parrot. "You were stupid enough to think you could sow and reap coins, like peas or beans! Honest money is earned by hard work, don't you know that?"

"Wh-what?" cried Pinocchio, clutching his wooden head. "I – I don't understand...."

"While you were in the town," explained the parrot, "the fox and the cat came back to this field, and they dug up those coins you buried! Then they both ran off like the wind!" Pinocchio could only stand there with his mouth open. But he never forgot the wise words of the parrot.

Carlo Collodi

1 Two Pigeons for Pedro Margarit

Melegari

After his discovery of America, Christopher Columbus built a fort on one of the islands, so that some of his men could defend the land. Among them was one called Pedro Margarit.

Soon, the fort was surrounded by natives, and Pedro and his friends reduced to starvation.

Then one day, a native crawled under a wall and gave Pedro two live pigeons.

Pedro accepted this gift and let the man go. Then he turned to his own men. "Two pigeons are not much to share between all of us," he said. "So, as I am your commander, I say that you give both of them to me!"

His men looked uneasily at each other for a few moments. It was clear they did not like the idea. Then the oldest stepped forward to speak.

"Agreed!" he said

And then Pedro opened the window and the pigeons flew up into the blue sky of the New World.

2 The Wild Cat and the Lair

Fedro

A Wild Cat once found a hollow in the trunk of an oak tree.

"This is the ideal lair for me and my little ones!" she thought. Then she noticed that higher up in the tree, an eagle had built a nest. And among the roots below, a wild boar had settled with her young.

The Wild Cat climbed up to the eagle's nest. "Hey!" she miaowed. "A wild boar has made her lair at the foot of this tree! She and her young are trying to make it fall, so they can eat everything up!"

And before the eagle could answer, she scrambled down to the home of the wild boar. "There's an eagle near the top of this tree!" she miaowed. "And she's already promised the eaglets lots of lovely steaks of wild boar!"

Well, the eagle and the wild boar both fled. But the Wild Cat and her young? They were quite happy and contented!

3 Baloo, the Bear

Kipling

Baloo is a bear friend of "man-cub" (that's what he calls children).

He teaches the law of the jungle to wolf cubs and other animals. He will teach it to you, so that you can go into the forest or the jungle in peace, eating roots and honey. Baloo likes children because, he says, "The man-cub can never do wrong!" Do you think that is true?

4 The Peasant and the Viper

Trilussa

A peasant was harvesting his corn one summer's day. Suddenly, he looked down and saw a viper on the ground. Another step, and he would have suffered a poisonous bite!

"I'll get you!" shouted the man. "You loathsome creature, lying in wait, ready to bite honest folk going about their work!"

"Well, that is what I have been doing since the world began," hissed the viper, "biting with my poisonous fang! It is my destiny! At least I am honest about it!"

"You?" spluttered the peasant. "Honest?"

"Yes!" said the snake. "If a man is not trusted, do you not say he is as slippery as an eel? Well, I am a viper! You know where you stand with me!"

"And now you know where you stand with me!" roared the man.

And with one blow from his scythe, he cut the viper in two.

5 The Ears of the Dromedary

Aesop

There was a time when the dromedary wanted a pair of horns like a bull's.

"What?" cried Mother Nature, "I have given you great height and the strength to cross deserts like the ships of men at sea! Now, you want horns, too?"

And she made the ears of a dromedary small and rounded, as different to long, pointed horns as anything could be!

6 The Polar Bear's Tail

an Eskimo legend

Many years ago, the Polar Bear had a lovely tail. He would lower it into the water to catch fish! But, as time passed, the fish got used to this. One day, the water iced over and the bear was trapped by his tail. He pulled and pulled – and pulled so hard that he left his tail behind.

And from that day to this, Polar Bears only have a little stump of a tail!

7 The Lion, the Wolf and the Fox

Aesop

Lion was feeling ill. But, as he lay in his cave, looking at all the animals, it gave him some comfort to know that he was their king. "Yes," he sighed, "everyone's here...."

"All except the fox, Your Majesty!" snarled the wolf spitefully. "Shame on him!"

But the fox had entered at that moment. He heard what the wolf had said.

"So! You have arrived!" roared the lion. "Why are you late?"

"Because," said the fox, "I went out to find you a cure!"

"Really?" said the lion. "What is it?"

"It's a cure made by skinning a live wolf!" growled the fox. "Then you wrap yourself up in the wolf's skin until you are nice and warm!"

"No!" howled the wolf. "Help!"

And so the wolf learned an important lesson. Those who plot against others often make trouble for themselves.

8 The Cheeky Young Cockerel

Florian

One day, a cockerel made a cheeky remark to a hen. She reached out and gave him a smack with her wing.

"Oh, leave him alone!" said the farm cockerel. "He is only young!"

"You can keep out of this!" said an old turkey, aiming a blow at the farm cockerel.

"Oh, leave him alone!" came the voice of the cheeky young cockerel. "He's getting old!"

9 The Camel, the Elephant and the Monkey

Aesop

The animals had met to decide who should be their king – a camel or an elephant. "The camel is never angry," said the monkey. "But a king has to make some animals fear him!"

Next minute, they saw the elephant flee from a little mouse, frightened to death! Then came a ROAR! It was the lion – YAWNING and showing his teeth! At once, the animals chose him as their king!

10 The Mouse and the Book

Alberti

There was a time when mice, who like to get their teeth into everything, began nibbling books as well.

Today, of course, there are so many books that if one gets nibbled, the world goes on just the same. But at the time of our story, books were very valuable. In those days, there were no films, no compact discs, cassette players or colour televisions.

Well, one mouse came across a huge book in a library. And as the book felt teeth sinking into its pages, it said, "Why do you eat me? There's all the knowledge in the whole world written in these pages!"

Now, the mouse could not spend much time in libraries – but he did know that all the knowledge in the whole world could not be written in a MILLION pages, however big.

So, he began to laugh. And when he had finished laughing, he started to nibble once more.

11 The Lizard and the Crocodile

Giorgi Bertola

"Honoured relative," the lizard said to the crocodile, "I have come many miles to see you! How clever you are to look like a log in the river!" The crocodile gave a grunt. "AND you can creep unseen through grass!" the lizard went on. "SUCH an honour to have a relation like you!"

"But – who are YOU?" grunted the crocodile. And he closed his eyes, ready to go to sleep.

12 Mother Lion and her cubs

Aesop

At the time when all creatures lived happily together, some young animals would often meet to play or talk together. They were all very proud of their families and never missed the chance of boasting a little. One day, they were discussing who had the most children.

"My mother has me and my three brothers!" announced one little puppy.

"And I was one of a brood of four baby birds!" said a duckling with pride.

"I can beat that!" said a pink little pig. "My mother gave birth to me and another nine piglets!"

The lioness had been sitting in the sun listening calmly.

"Your mothers should be very proud!" she said.

"How many children do you have?" asked the puppy.

"Only one," purred the lioness. "But that one is a lion!" And the moral of this story is – quality matters more than quantity.

13 The Dog and the Eskimo

Melegari

A dog was pulling an eskimo on his sledge. "Get a move on!" the man yelled, cracking a whip.

"I must stop!" the dog panted.

The eskimo got off the sledge. "I told you to get a move on," he shouted, "because the bears are coming!"

"That's lucky!" said the dog. "Bears are faster than dogs over the snow! Get the first one here to pull the sledge, and we'll soon be home!" The eskimo thought for a moment.

"How do you know the bear will pull the sledge, and not eat both of us instead?" he asked.

"Simple!" said the dog. "I know one who will do it! Shall I go and fetch him?"

"Oh, why didn't you say so before?" snapped the eskimo. He untied the dog from the sledge.

"Go on!" he shouted. "And hurry up!"

The dog ran off. And the eskimo never saw him again.

14 The Camel, Man's Friend

Aesop

If you are afraid of something, the best idea is to get used to it. Then the fear goes. This is what happened to the first men who met the camel. At first, they were frightened because of its size. But little by little, they realised that instead of being fierce, the camel was as gentle as an ox. They put reins and a saddle on its body, and even trusted it with small children.

15 The Spider and the Keyhole

Leonardo da Vinci

A spider wanted to spin a web in a safe place. "A nice, quiet place!" he was always saying. "That's what I need!" And one day, he was able to say, "Right! This is it!"

It was a keyhole in the door of a lumber-room, which was hardly ever opened. And when anyone did open it, the keyhole was never used – simply because nobody ever knew where the key was.

Flies went through the keyhole by day and wasps and moths by night. It seemed the spider would never be short of food.

So he went into the keyhole, spun his web and prepared to settle in his new home.

But – disaster soon struck! It came in the form of a new key which had been cut to fit the lock. Just one half-turn destroyed everything – including the spider! And just as a key is found to all locks, so a key is found to all mysteries, sooner or later.

16 The Butterfly and the Poet

Lamartine

A poet and a wise man were watching a butterfly. "A lovely creature," sighed the poet. "Born when the rose blooms, dying as it fades, kissing the flowers...."

"It is like the wishes of men," said the wise man "clinging to this and that, going from one wish to another, not understanding that happiness is to be content in finding peace wherever we are."

17 The Bear of Berne

Melegari

On the Coat of Arms of Berne, capital of Switzerland, there is a bear. Its name comes from the German word *Bar*, pronounced "bear". And that is why the people of Berne compare themselves to the bear. "We are strong," they will say, "peaceful and easy-going!"

"And that is why you sway as you walk!" other Swiss people add.

18 Theresa and the Lively Butterfly

Sailer

Theresa was a lovely little girl. One day, she was running through a field, when a lively butterfly fluttered right under her nose.

It passed once, then twice. And the moment Theresa saw it, she reached out and grabbed it in her hand.

Of course, this was not the right thing to do. Butterflies flutter around for everyone to see and enjoy.

Theresa was very pleased about catching the butterfly. "I've got you!" she squealed. "Let me go!" squeaked the butterfly. "What harm have I done to be treated like this?"

Theresa stopped, suddenly ashamed. Had she really heard the butterfly pleading with her? Nobody will ever know. The fact is that it slipped from Theresa's fingers and began fluttering again. And all Theresa had to show for it were a few coloured flakes on her fingers.

19 The Wild Boar and the Monkey

Melegari

There is a tale that as he explored America, Columbus and his men came across a wild boar and a monkey having a battle. The explorers moved closer, trying to see why the two animals were fighting. At once, the wild boar and the monkey went to attack the men. This shows that although two beings may fight, they will unite against a common enemy.

20 The Fox and the Prawn

Afanasjev

A fox once challenged a prawn in a stream to a race.

"All right!" said the prawn.

They agreed on the finishing line – a log which someone had put as a bridge across the stream – and prepared themselves for the start.

"Ready! Steady! GO!" cried the fox. He was looking forward to an easy win! But he did not know that the prawn could jump in and out of the water, balancing on the end of its tail.

"I must win!" thought the fox. "I can't let a little thing like a prawn beat me!"

Very soon, he came up to the finish. And the moment his tail touched the log, he turned towards the starting point.

"Didn't I say I'd win?" he yelled. "Well, I'm on the bridge! Where are you, prawn?"

"Here," said the prawn. "At the finish, with you! It isn't always the biggest who wins a race!"

21 The King and the Falcon

Tolstoy

Falconry was once very popular. The falconer kept a falcon on his gloved hand. When he saw a bird flying, he would throw the falcon into flight to catch it.

Many kings were keen falconers. One stopped at a fountain to enjoy a cool drink – until the falcon knocked the cup from the king's hand with its claw. And when he filled it again, the same thing happened.

"Throw this bird to the dogs!" the king shouted. He was very annoyed.

But as a servant took the falcon away, a royal messenger came galloping up.

"Majesty!" he cried. "Do not drink that water! The fountain is poisonous!"

Those we trust are not always able to help us in ways we understand. This fable does not say whether the king had time to save the life of the falcon – but we hope that he did.

February

22 The Bear and the Cloud of Wool

a legend from Norway

Norwegian legend says that the first clouds were made of wool!

One day, some wisps floated down into a wood, where nymphs lived among the trees by day, and danced by the moon. One nymph picked up the wisps of wool, weaving them with some grass to make a cradle for her baby. The baby grew so big and so woolly that it was called – Bear. And, who knows? Perhaps it really was!

23 The Nettle and the Butterfly

Melegari

"Nobody likes me because of my sting!" said a nettle to Mother Nature. "What can I do to make just one friend?"

"I'll see what I can do!" promised Mother Nature.

At first, nothing happened. Then one day, a Red Admiral, one of the most beautiful butterflies in the world, fluttered down on a leaf!

"I am hunted by people and chased by birds!" said the Red Admiral. "May I shelter here, among your leaves?"

"Of course," said the nettle, not really expecting the Red Admiral to stay. But from then on, those lovely butterflies always laid their eggs in the nettles – and three times a year, stinging nettles nourish and protect Red Admiral caterpillars. Now, if anyone calls a nettle an ugly plant with a sting, it smiles to itself. "Yes, I do sting. But – just see where the Red Admiral butterflies hide their young!"

24 The Dog and the Crocodile

Fedro

The River Nile in Egypt is home to lots of crocodiles! One hot day, a dog was on the bank having a drink when a crocodile appeared, snapping his jaws. The dog began running, taking a few laps when he could.

"Why run?" said the crocodile. "Much better for you to stand still while you drink!"

"Better to keep my skin, as well!" answered the dog.

25 Why the Raven is Black

a story from Romania

This story says that the raven was white when Noah sent it from the ark to look around the flooded world. The bird flew around eating all sorts of rubbish for three days and nights before returning.

"Flying around for three days and three nights in the dark, eating rubbish!" cried Noah. "From now on, you will be as dark as night, and eat food that others leave behind!"

26 The Moon, the Rose and the Nightingale

Novaro

Some people say that if you want something, you have to beg and plead. Others believe something comes just by waiting. Listen to this story, and see what you think.

One evening, a nightingale began to sing, as she always did, her little beak lifted to the sky. Out came the moon, as beautiful as ever, her face glowing in a golden light.

The nightingale stopped singing, quite spellbound.

"Kiss me!" the roses begged the moon, one after the other.

"I'm the most beautiful!" cried another rose. "Kiss me!"

"No, I'm the loveliest rose!" cried a third. "Kiss me!"

So many voices all at once made the moon shrink back and hide behind a cloud. But moments later, she sent down a moonbeam, kissing the nightingale with its beautiful golden ray. Yet, the nightingale had said nothing.

27 The Ant who was Silly

Melegari

"Are you coming out?" an ant shouted at an elephant who was swimming in the lake.

"Go away!" cried the elephant.

"But you MUST come out!" cried the ant.

"Well?" roared the mighty elephant as he came out of the water. "What do you want?"

"Er..." mumbled the ant. "I wondered if you'd picked up my swimsuit by mistake!"

28 The Lizard and the Iguanadon

Melegari

A lizard once found himself in a Museum of Natural History, among the prehistoric animals!

"Hey, insect!" thundered a voice high above. "How dare you copy me?"

It was an iguanadon – a lizard a thousand times bigger than he was, looking so proud and haughty!

"I'm NOT an insect!" said the lizard. "I'm a reptile!"

"Rubbish!" laughed the iguanadon, making the windows shake. "I'M a reptile! The plesiosaur is a reptile, the dinosaur, too! Look at our armour, our long sharp teeth! We once roamed the earth –"

"I-I know!" said the lizard hastily. "And I confess that I would like to be bigger! But then," he added, "how could I enter my little home where I am so happy?" The iguanadon did not answer.

"So," ended the little lizard, "I think I'll stay just the way I am!"

29 The Lion and the Three Oxen

Aesop

A lion had been after three oxen for a long time. But as they stayed good friends, he knew that if he attacked one, the other two would defend their friend with their horns. So he made up his mind to split them up, talking first to just one of them. "Do you know what one of your friends says about you? That you are a greedy ox, wanting all best grass for yourself!"

"Hah!" roared the ox. Deep inside, he began to doubt the loyalty of his two friends.

Then the lion went off and said exactly the same thing to the other two oxen.

The result was that their friendship came to an end and they split up. And without any defence, the lion was able to catch one after the other.

How wonderful it would be if nobody believed their enemies and stayed true to their friends! Then we would all know the truth of the saying, "Keep strong together!"

The Wolf, the Fox and the Cheese

ONE evening as the sun was setting, a wolf prowled around feeling very hungry. So, he was not at all pleased to see the fox, trotting off towards his lair with a plump hen in his mouth and looking forward to a fine feast!

"Hands up!" roared the wolf. "Drop that chicken!"

The fox let the chicken fall to the ground – but the wolf noticed he kept a paw on top.

"Look," said the fox, "this chicken is only fit for an animal with a weak stomach like mine! For a strong beast like you with such a good appetite, it's only a starter! Instead of satisfying your hunger, it will only make you hungrier still!"

"Never mind the speech!" roared the wolf. "Just leave the chicken and go!"

"Very well," sighed the fox. "I shall have to be satisfied just having the cheese!"

"Cheese?" said the wolf sharply. "What cheese?"

"Steady on!" cried the fox. "You wouldn't want to make me die of hunger, would you?"

"I haven't tasted cheese for ages!" snarled the wolf. "Now you've made me want some!"

"All right!" said the fox. "You have the cheese – and I'll keep the chicken!"

"Very well!" agreed the wolf. "We'll hide the chicken, then you can show me the cheese! And if I like the look of it, you can come back and pick up the chicken!"

"Agreed!" said the fox, hiding the chicken under some leaves.

"Mind you," the wolf went on, "if the cheese doesn't taste good, I'LL get the chicken, and YOU'LL get a beating!"

"Agreed!" said the fox again, eyes sparkling with mischief.

Off they went across the fields, the fox in front and the wolf behind, both feeling hungry and neither trusting the other at all.

"Wouldn't he like to know what I'm thinking!" thought the fox.

"If he thinks he's going to trick me," thought the wolf, "he's going to be mistaken!"

As they went along, the sun finally set and the sky grew dark. Night fell and the moon appeared, round and golden.

"Here we are!" announced the fox suddenly. He stretched out a paw towards a well. And, at the bottom of that well, the wolf could see something big and round and yellow!

"Is that the cheese?" he breathed.

"Of course it's the cheese!" said the fox. "Go and get it!"

"No, wait!" said the wolf, stepping back a little. "You go down first! And if you don't bring it up, then I'll go down, too!"

Now, on the well was a pulley with a rope wound around it. And at each end of the rope, there was a bucket – so that, when water was being drawn, one bucket went down empty and the other rose up, full of water. At night-time, of course, they were both empty, and were left on the edge of the well.

The fox got into the bucket and lowered himself into the well. When he reached the bottom, he crouched down in the darkness. Minutes passed.

"Come on!" yelled the wolf at last. "Where's that cheese?"

"Urgh – urgh –" answered the fox, pretending to be struggling. "I-I can't – urgh – lift it! It's – urgh – it's too heavy! Ooh, the smell of fresh cheese! Come down and give me a hand, wolf! There's enough here for the most wonderful feed!"

"That cheese is mine!" howled the wolf. "Get your paws off!" He jumped into the second bucket and lowered himself into the well.

And, as he went down, the wolf saw the fox, rising up in the other bucket. Had he been tricked, after all?

He was still wondering as he plunged to the bottom of the well and felt the water gurgling round his feet, with the reflection of the big, round, cheesy-yellow moon....

"Cheerio," cried the fox from the edge of the well. "I'm off to collect my chicken! Maybe I'll come back and throw you a few bones!"

From a traditional folk tale.

1 The Dog, the Cat and the Bear

Aesop

Cats and dogs are not always enemies.

This is a story about a cat and a dog who were good friends. They were out walking together one day, when there suddenly appeared a bear! The cat jumped up into a tree for safety. But the dog, not being able to do this, threw himself on the ground and pretended to be dead. He knew that the bear would not eat the meat of a dead animal.

But the bear began sniffing all round the dog, again and again. At one point it seemed to the cat that the bear was whispering something in the dog's ear!

Still the dog did not move. At last, the bear went off and the cat came down from the tree.

"What did the bear whisper in your ear?" she asked the dog.

"He told me," said the dog, "not to go out with a friend who would leave me to face danger alone!"

2 The Mouth of the Eel

Melegari

One day, Mother Nature became a tuna fish so that she could go under the sea. And what did she find? Man's first fishing net!

She swam into the net, making a big hole so that the fish could escape. Then she found that she was caught fast!

Next moment, along came a shoal of eels, which – as you may know – leave the rivers once a year and return to the sea, swimming great distances in the oceans.

One eel saw the tuna fish caught in the net. He broke away from the shoal and swam up beside the tuna fish, chewing and nibbling at the net until the fish was free.

Mother Nature was very grateful to that eel! "You know how to use your teeth!" she said. "From now on, your young ones will be born with all their teeth!"

And so it was. When they hatch, a baby eel may be only three millimetres long – but already it has all its teeth!

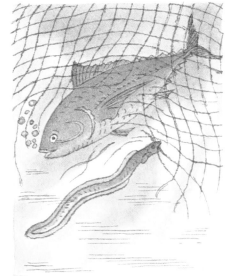

3 The Singing Cockerel

from Norway

Each morning, a cockerel would sit on a fence, singing his heart out. "Cock-a-Doodle-Dooooo! Cock-a-Doodle-Dooooo!"

Everyone could hear him for miles around, all thinking what a powerful, strong voice he had! One day, this singing cockerel had just finished his first song of the day, when, out of the corner of his eye, he saw the fox approaching.

The singing cockerel was pleased when the fox smiled and gave a little bow.

"What a voice you have!" he said. "It reminds me of your grandfather! He could sing standing on one leg and with his eyes closed!"

"Really?" crowed the cockerel. "I must try that!"

The cockerel lifted one leg, closed his eyes, and – ZAP! – he was snatched up by the fox!

The moral of this story? If you want to make a song and dance, it's best to choose your audience!

4 The Fox, the Wolf and the Fishmonger

Gesta Romanorum

The fox could smell a fish-cart coming! And he liked fish! So, he laid down in the road, pretending to be dead.

The cart came along and the fishmonger got down, thinking the fox really was dead. "I'll take this fox!" he said "I can always sell the fur!"

He threw the fox among the baskets of fish and drove on – leaving the fox to eat bream, mackerel, whitebait and prawns!

Then the fox wrapped two eels around his neck and jumped out, laughing at the fishmonger.

Soon, the wolf came along. "What nice eels!" he snarled.

"Lots of them in that cart!" said the fox. And as soon as he told his story, the wolf ran off and laid in the road.

The man stopped the cart and got down. "Lovely fur!" he said. "Is he dead like the fox?"

"Yes!" said the wolf. But, as the fishmonger chased him away, it was clear that wolf was very much alive!

5 The Swallow's "Good-Night!"

Novaro

To see a flight of swallows at sunset is a beautiful sight, rising higher and higher until they seem to disappear, just before the first starlight.

It is said that swallows do this to wish "Good-Night!" to God in Heaven.

Then they return to their nests and with God's smile reflected in their eyes, they lay their heads down on their hearts and sleep until dawn.

6 A Parrot of Few Words

from India

There was once a parrot who could only say one thing – "No doubt about it!" In the end its owner decided to sell it.

"How much do you want?" asked a learned professor.

"Shall we say – one hundred crowns?" suggested the owner.

A hundred crowns was a lot of money to the professor. He thought for a moment. Then he turned to the parrot. "Would you say you are worth one hundred crowns?" he asked.

"No doubt about it!" said the parrot at once.

It seemed a very wise answer to the learned professor! He counted out the money, well pleased with his purchase – until he had heard the same answer to a hundred different questions!

In the end, the professor flew into a rage. "What a fool I was," he stormed, "to fall for such a trick!"

And – can you guess what the parrot said?

"No doubt about it!"

7 The Polecat and the Hare

Melegari

A polecat was about to eat a hare – when the hare managed to cry, "Bless Your Father!"

The polecat stopped. "My father?" he repeated.

"Yes!" said the hare. "Such a saintly animal! Before eating, he always put his paws together to say Grace!"

"What? Like this?" said the polecat. And as he put his paws together, the hare leapt to safety!

8 The Wolf in the Well

Gesta Romanorum

A thirsty fox saw a bucket at the edge of a well. So he got inside and went down to the bottom – as another bucket (which was empty) rose up to the top.

It was only when he'd had his drink that he realised he could not get out of the well! "What are you doing down there, Fox?" It was the wolf.

"I'm dead and I've gone to Heaven!" was the answer.

"Really?" the wolf sniggered.

"Come and see!" cried the fox. "Heaven is full of lambs and hens and chickens."

"I'm on my way!" cried the wolf, jumping into the second bucket and going down fast.

"Hello!" came the voice of the fox on his way up, as the two buckets met halfway. At the top of the well, he jumped out! But the wolf had to wait for people to come and draw water. And when they found him in the bucket, he wished he had stayed where he was!

9 The Horse and the Camel

Lessing

"People think I'm a beautiful animal," a horse said to Mother Nature. "But maybe some parts of my body could be better!"

"Really?" said Mother Nature.

"Yes! I think my nostrils are a bit too large. And although my coat can be many different colours – white, black, grey, tawny-brown, piebald, or even with black spots – my feet are too big and heavy! If they were more slender, they would be much faster! And what about giving me a long neck, like a swan? And a different sort of back, so that I don't have to carry riders all the time?"

"So," said Mother Nature "is this how you'd like to look?" She waved her hand. And, little by little, there appeared – a camel!

"No!" cried the horse! And ran away!

And ever since, if a horse should meet a camel, it shivers with fear and runs off.

10 The Hare and the Elephant

from India

"The little dear!" cried the animals when they saw the baby elephant.

"What a great big lump!" they said when they saw the hare. "Everyone says I am big, and YOU are small!" said the hare. "So, if you want anything done –"

"Yes!" cried the elephant. "You can iron the skin of your big back on my little foot!"

So – we may be big in one group, yet small in another.

11 The Fly, the Spider and the Housemaid

Sailer

A housemaid was busy with her work, when a fly came buzzing around. It flew around the end of her nose, then round the tip of her feather-duster – and then she watched it flying up towards the corner of the room where a spider had woven its web.

Next minute, the fly was caught in the web. And the more it tried to struggle free, the more it got tangled up in the web.

"Ha-ha-ha!" chuckled the spider, already looking forward to a great feed.

But when the spider saw the housemaid's hand starting to get nearer and nearer, it began to shake and tremble, feeling just as the fly had done moments before. The spider thought it was so strong when it caught that little fly.

But it cowered with fear when its web was destroyed by the housemaid with one finger.

12 How eels were born

Melegari

In the Bible you can find the story of Samson, a man who used his strength to defend others. One of his enemies found out that Samson got his strength through his long hair. So to deprive him of his strength, his hair was cut as he slept. And, as he was taken prisoner, legend says that his long hair fell into the waters of a stream which flowed into a river, where they became eels.

13 Advice for the Wolf

Trilussa

The wolf was in a bad mood! "There are some sheep who go around saying I steal too much!" he told Mother Nature. "I want something done to put an end to this gossip, because it blackens my good name!"

"Something can be done right away!" smiled Mother Nature.

"Really?" The wolf was very pleased! "What is that?"

"Don't steal at all!" came the reply.

14 The Years of Man

Aesop

Man is living longer these days. But for other animals, life is harder and shorter. Stories from ancient times also show us how man's intelligence often turned to cunning when it came to dealing with his four-legged friends.

Legend tells us that when man was created, he thought that his life on earth would be short. And when the first winter came, he set to work and built a shelter, to protect himself against the bitter weather.

Soon there came a knock at the door. It was the horse.

"I am so hungry!" he said to the man. "And it is snowing hard! Can I shelter under your roof?"

"Very well!" said the man. "But in return you must give me some years of your life!"

The horse was so cold, he agreed at once. So did the ox, who arrived a little later on.

Then there came another knock at the door.

"It's the dog!" cried a voice. "Please, give me shelter!"

He was allowed in – but only after he had given the man some years of his life.

And from this we see the shape of a man's life. During the years given him by the horse, he is full of life and energy. Then comes the years of the ox, when man can only take charge. And at last come the years when he talks and talks without stopping – just like a dog barking.

15 The Mammoth and Noah

an Eskimo legend

When Noah built his ark, only the mammoths did not go on board. "We're so big and mighty!" they said. "No matter how much rain falls, we shall never be covered!"

But when the earth was flooded, they all disappeared.

"Well," sighed Noah, as he looked around after the flood, "we now have fewer proud creatures on earth!"

16 Mother Fox is sorry

Gay

Mother Fox was feeling ill. "My sons," she said to her cubs, "maybe I shall not last much longer. And now, I am having nightmares thinking about all the poor creatures I have eaten... chickens, ducks, turkeys, geese... so many poor victims of my greed!"

Just then came the cry of a guinea-fowl. Mother Fox gave a start and closed her eyes.

The sound of the guinea-fowl came again, nearer this time. She opened her eyes, and sat up in bed. "That's it!" she cried, pointing. "That's what I need to get rid of my nightmare!"

How she smiled as her sons went out of the lair. She smiled even more when they came back with a guinea-fowl as a cure for their poor, sick mother.

This story shows that we cannot always believe those who say they are sorry....

17 The Cat and the Eagle

Trilussa

Once the eagle saw himself on Coats-of-Arms, flags, coins and medals, he began feeling very proud and conceited. "Men see me as a symbol of strength and beauty!" he kept saying. "No bird is better than me!"

"That's what you think!" said the cat at last. "Just now in the kitchen I heard a man say he liked a chicken better than anything else!"

18 The Coyote in the Helmet

Melegari

Going through a desert where there had been a battle, a coyote found a magnificent-looking helmet!

The coyote put the helmet on and returned to his pack as fast as he could. "Coyotes, fall in!" he roared, standing on a rock.

The other coyotes did not seem very impressed. "All in a line!" shouted the coyote, tapping his fine helmet. "I am your general!"

None of them moved. The coyote began getting very annoyed. "Don't you see this helmet on my head?" he raged. "Do you know what it means?"

The oldest coyote went up to him. "There is a saying," he said, "that clothes cannot make a king! So a helmet cannot make a general!"

The coyote tried hard to understand what that meant. But as the sun beat down on his fine helmet, it seemed as though his brains were being roasted!

19 The Ass and the Ox

from A Thousand and One Nights

The ox and the ass worked for the same master. The ox toiled in the fields all day – but the ass just took the master to the market once a week.

One evening, the ass gave the ox a little bit of advice. "At our meal-time," he said, "don't touch any food! See what happens!"

Well, the master thought the ox had not eaten because he felt ill, So, he took the ass out to work in the fields.

"What hard work this is!" thought the ass. "Good thing it is only for one day!"

But the ox pretended to be off his food for another day, and then another – until one evening, the ass whispered: "Guess what I heard the master telling his friend!"

"Tell me!" said the ox.

"If that ox is no better tomorrow, I'll have him made into beef-steaks!"

The ox shook with terror. And the next day, it was the ass who was taking a rest!

20 The Cockerel and the Admiring Fox

Pulci

"Hey!" cried a fox, seeing a cockerel in a tree. "What are you doing up there?"

"Singing!" the cockerel crowed. "Can't you hear?" To the fox, it sounded like a motorbike driving away!

"Can't you sing any louder?" he asked. "Or maybe come down a bit lower, so I can hear!"

So, the cockerel hopped on to a lower branch and began singing again. Leaves fell, ants, worms and hornets scurried for shelter – and in one sparrow's nest, three eggs split open!

"What a wonderful voice!" smiled the fox. "Come lower so that I can hear better!"

So the cockerel came down on to a lower branch, closing his eyes with the first notes of his shrill song.

Now, you might hope that the cockerel tricked the fox. But, no! The fox ran off with that cockerel! He wished then that he hadn't listened to so much praise from a crafty customer!

21 The Donkey and the Singing Cricket

Aesop

A donkey pricked up its long ears one summer's day, listening to the lovely sound of a cricket singing in the sun. He could not help wishing he could sing too. "What is the secret of your fine voice?" he asked.

"Dew!" said the cricket. "The little drops of water which fall on the grass in the early hours of a new day!"

"I know!" cried the ass. And with a loud bray, he thanked the cricket excitedly.

Next morning at dawn, the donkey was in the middle of the meadow with his tongue stretched out between his teeth, waiting for the first drops of dew. He did not know that dew cannot be collected in such a way. Day after day, he stood there, until he became ill and died of hunger.

A donkey was never meant to sing like a cricket. And those who want something which is not natural to them, run the greatest risk of disaster.

22 The Story of the Microbe

Melegari

A microbe is a tiny, living being – it can be a plant or an animal. Microbes exist in bacteria. Some bacteria cause disease. Some fight infections and help yeast to make bread rise and ale brew. Usually, a tiny microbe can only be seen by its family. But – if you should see a black spot on a photo or film – chances are that same little microbe landed on a camera lens!

23 The Ant and the Dove

Steinhovel

A thirsty ant was scurrying towards a well, hoping for a cool drink. She crawled inside and put her head down towards the water.... But, because of their big pincers and jaws an ant's head is heavier than the rest of its body. So, as she put her head down the steep wall of the well, its weight dragged the rest of her tiny body with it – and down she fell into the water.

She would have drowned, if a dove on the branch of a tree above had not broken off a leafy twig with its beak and thrown it down into the water.

The ant floated on the leaf to the wall of the well and climbed to safety – just as a peasant woman was aiming a catapult at the dove! When the ant bit the woman on her bare ankle, she gave a cry, dropped the catapult – and the dove flew to safety.

So, as you see, one good turn deserves another.

24 The Judgement of the Gorilla

La Fontaine

Wolf had accused Fox of robbing him. So, the gorilla was sent for to decide who was guilty. "Wolf is guilty of saying he had been robbed before Fox could defend himself!" he said. "And Fox is guilty because he stole from the wolf!"

"That's not fair!" cried Wolf.

"Yes it is," said the gorilla. "By saying you are both guilty, I cannot make any mistake!"

25 The Fly who was Jealous

Trilussa

A fly was jealous of a butterfly's beautiful wings. "When people see you among the flowers," it said, "do they remember that you in all your glory and me with my plain wings, both began life as grubs – me as a maggot, and you as a caterpillar!"

"Maybe!" said the butterfly. "Then they remember that I was born among the roses. And you were born among the rubbish!"

26 Father Horse and the little Colt

Florian

Father Horse and his colt lived in a meadow with plenty of grass and fresh water, and lots of space for a gallop. But the colt was not satisfied. He kept saying he needed a change of air – until, at last, Father Horse decided they should move on. They toiled up windy hills, through clusters of rocks which tore at their hooves, and crossed plains so hot and dry, it seemed they would die of thirst. Gallops changed to trotting. Trotting became a walk. Then Father Horse decided to take a road he knew well.

By night-fall, the colt was eating grass and drinking clear water. "What a nice place!" he said. "Let's stay here!"

At daybreak, the colt saw it was the meadow where he had been born!

"Let this be a lesson to you my son!" said Father Horse. "Never forget to be grateful for all you have!"

27 The Mouse in the Trap

Melegari

A mouse was enjoying himself in a big kitchen, until a cat came along! Away he ran – but when he saw a fine piece of cheese he reached out a paw, and, SNAP! He was caught in a trap!

"You've been beaten now!" said the cat.

"Perhaps!" squeaked the mouse. "But where there is life, there is hope!" And he began to nibble the cheese!

28 The Donkey and the Dog

La Fontaine

A donkey and a dog were going to market with their master. It was a very long walk along rough roads. At last their master decided to go into a field for a rest.

He unloaded the donkey, set the dog free and settled down in the shade of a tree for a nice, long nap.

Very soon, the donkey began to chew at the grass. But there was nothing for the dog to eat.

"Look," he said, "you can see some bread among the load you were carrying! Couldn't we take just one piece?"

"Wait until the master wakes up," said the donkey. "He'll give you some!" And he went on eating the fresh grass.

Just then there came the roar of the wolf. "Arrrgh!"

"Help me!" brayed the donkey. "Help me, dog!"

"I'm so hungry, I do not have the strength!" said the dog. "Wait until the master wakes up! He will help you!"

29 The Crab and the Dog

Aesop

There was once a crab who was tired of living in the sea.

"I would be happier living on this beach!" he thought. He looked at the clear, blue sky, the sun sparkling on the rocks where the sea-birds landed, delighted with all that he saw. "Others can stay in the sea!" he thought. "I shall enjoy the beautiful sun, and –"

But at that very moment, he found himself wedged between the teeth of a dog!

"This is my own fault!" the crab told himself. "I should have stayed where I belonged! I am a sea creature, not a land animal!"

But he did not know that the dog was thinking, "Why did I ever come down here from the city, just to eat fish, like the cat? This shell is so hard and salty! Ugh!"

He spat the crab out on to the breakwater, where the sea met the beach. And after that the crab never came out from beneath the waves again.

30 The Legion of the Lark

Melegari

A lark was returning to her nest one evening when she saw something glinting in the tall grass. It was another lark!

"Who are you?" she cried.

"A lark made of bronze," said the other, "fallen from a soldier's helmet! Julius Caesar made me the sign of a legion of Roman soldiers, which is why they are called The Legion of the Lark!"

"We'll catch them up!" said the first lark. She took the bronze lark in her beak, flying until she saw the legion of marching soldiers. Seeing one soldier with a lark badge missing, the lark flew down and dropped the bronze lark to the ground.

"Ye Gods!" cried the soldier. "I must not lose my lark!" And, still marching, he kissed the bronze lark and put it safely back on the point of his helmet. The first lark flew into the sky, singing a last song to the legion before flying off home.

31 The Home of the Little Mouse

Afanasjev

A little mouse was looking for a home. And when he saw a great, big pumpkin, it seemed a lovely house to him! He bit into the skin, and put his little head inside. "Anyone at home?" he shouted. There was no answer. So he moved in there and then.

But the pumpkin house was too big for him. So, when a frog came to the door and cried, "Anyone at home?" the little mouse called "Come in!" And the frog settled in, too!

Still there was a lot of space inside that great, big pumpkin! There was room for a hare, then a fox – and even a wolf!

But when a bear came along, they all decided there was no room for him. The bear was very upset. He sat down on the pumpkin, and – SPLAT! That was the end of the home of the mouse, the frog, the hare, the fox and the wolf. The pumpkin house had certainly NOT been too big for the bear!

The Town Mouse and the Country Mouse

THE country mouse had invited the town mouse to visit him. He met his friend at the edge of the field and took him back to his home, in the hollow at the foot of a big oak tree.

Inside, the town mouse began sniffing the air, hoping for something good to eat.

"What a delicious smell!" he remarked – although, to him, it did not smell delicious at all. But he was a very polite town mouse .

"Oh, it's nothing!" smiled the country mouse. "Just corn broth!"

"Lovely!" exclaimed the town mouse, trying to remember exactly what corn was. He sat down at the table.

"You can always depend on corn broth for a good meal!" said the country mouse, ladling out the broth for his friend.

The town mouse wiped his forehead with a silk handkerchief, closed his eyes, took a deep breath – and gulped down enough big spoonfuls to empty his plate. The country mouse was pleased!

"The grains of corn are very much like the grains of wheat!" he said. "But of course I can tell the difference! What about you?"

"Well – er – I-I –" stammered the town mouse, pushing his plate away. "Is there anything else?"

"Oh, yes!" cried the country mouse. He pushed the plate back. "You know, in the country we only use one plate for all our food. We're simple folk here. Now, have a little more –"

"No, thank you!" the town-mouse blurted out. "Er – I think we shall eat at my house next time! I have a nice, juicy ham, all ready to eat..."

"That will be nice," murmured the country mouse.

The town mouse said nothing more – just put his scarf around his neck and pulled his hat down over his eyes.

A little while afterwards, the country mouse left the hollow of the great oak tree to meet the town mouse.

He was taken to a beautiful house in the centre of town,

where his friend lived.

"Look up there!" whispered the town mouse, pointing to an enormous ham which hung from the ceiling of the larder.

"I'll go up," the town mouse continued, "and nibble through that string! Then you can taste something better than plain corn! Better than bread crumbs or anything like that! We don't eat like chickens, here in the town!"

Scrambling up the side of a big flask, on to the shelves, then along the shelves to a rope stretched between one wall and the other, the town mouse climbed up to the ceiling and began nibbling at the string which held the ham.

BOMP! With the string broken, the ham fell on the floor. The town mouse jumped down to the ground and put a finger to his lips, winking at the country mouse in the dark.

"Hey!" came a man's voice. "What's going on in there?"

"Time to go!" whispered the town mouse. He scampered down into his hole, closely followed by the country mouse!

Clutching each other in terror, eyes wide in fear, they heard the larder door opening and the man going inside.

There was the sound of the man picking up the ham. "There must be a mouse in this larder!" he said. "He thinks he's clever, nibbling the string to make the ham fall down so that he can eat it! From now on, I'm putting the cat in here!"

Just then there came a soft, scratching sound and the man felt something pass over his shoe. "There he is!" he shouted to the cat. "Get him!"

But the country mouse – for it was he who had escaped – had already reached the safety of the street. With no ham to eat and a long run back home to the country, he would be glad of his simple supper of corn broth. And he would rather have that, he decided, than all the delicious ham and other treats to be found in a big town.

Aesop

1 The Wolf, the Goat and the Little Kids

Afanasjev

Mother Goat and her kids lived in a little cottage in the woods. Here, the kids were quite safe whilst she went to get food.

There was a wolf in the neighbourhood. So Mother Goat told her children not to open the door until they heard her voice calling from outside:

"Open the door, your Mother is here! Now I am home, There is nothing to fear!"

One day, the wolf heard Mother Goat's words. He waited a while before knocking on the door, calling:

"Open the door, children dear! You are quite safe! Your Mother is here!"

"You're not our mother!" cried the kids. "She has a soft, little voice. The words aren't right, either!" And they kept the door shut.

And so the wolf found himself as hungry as ever! But in a little while, you shall learn what happened next.....

2 The Crow and the Dog

Melegari

The crow, like owls and other birds, is often regarded as a sign of bad luck. Was this what the dog in this story thought? There he was, peacefully chewing on some scraps of meat, when he saw that crow swooping down towards him. "Hey!" squawked the crow. "That meat looks good!"

The dog went on eating.

The crow decided to try something else. "Many men say that the dog is a very intelligent animal!" he croaked. "Is that true?"

The dog took care to keep the meat between his paws. But he lifted his head and said, "Yes! It is!"

Just then, another crow pecked at his tail. The dog jumped up, turned around – and by then the first crow had flown away with the meat in his beak, the second crow following on to get his share. So, it seems there is more than one way of being clever!

3 The Considerate Spider

Trilussa

Hearing the buzzing of an insect, a spider crouched in his web. He strained his ears, hoping it was getting nearer.

He heard a shuffling sound, a clatter, then a deep thud – and the humming stopped. The insect had been killed with the blow of a broom.

"How very cruel!" thought the spider. "Disgraceful!" But then he wondered, "Now, what am I going to eat?"

4 The Mystery of the Eel

Melegari

"Something's upsetting me!" an eel told Mother Nature.

"What is it?" she sighed. "You are a fish who can feel at ease in water, or in mud at the bottom of holes. And though you live poorly for many years, eating food like bits of potatoes and grains of barley, in the end, you see the world, swimming thousands of kilometres, crawling under trees and climbing up beneath the roofs of houses. What else do you want?"

"Well," said the eel, "I do not mind finishing up in a cook-pot. But I hate men saying, 'As slippery as an eel!' as if an eel cannot be trusted."

"It is unfair!" agreed Mother Nature. "And to pay men back for what they say about you, I shall see that they never discover the part of the ocean where eels go once a year."

And, so it is. For men, half the life of an eel is indeed a mystery.

5 The Mouse and the Snail

Melegari

"No wonder you're so slow!" a mouse once laughed at a snail. "Fancy having to carry your house everywhere you go!"

"Look at me!" the mouse went on. "The distance you go in one hour, I can cover with the speed of a rocket!"

"I know," said the snail. "But as Mother Nature has given the same speed to a cat – wouldn't you sometimes like a safe shelter like mine?"

April

6 The Ivy and the Lizard

Melegari

"You worry me," an ivy said to a lizard one day, "living under stones and among weeds! Wouldn't you rather be like me, climbing the trunk of an oak tree, towards the sky?"

"Your life may seem better than mine," said the lizard after some thought. "But I do not depend on anyone. Without the oak to feed and support you, I think you would be worse off than me!"

7 The Bat and the Two Weasels

Aesop

One day, a bat was flitting around when he hurt his wing on a wall and fell down, right in front of a weasel's lair. The weasel came out at once, shouting at the top of her voice. "How dare you come here, you horrible mouse!"

The weasel would have eaten the bat there and then, if he had not given a loud squeak. "I – I am not a mouse!" he blabbered. Would the weasel believe him, he wondered? "Can't you see my wings? I am a bird!"

Very well!" hissed the weasel after a pause. "You can go! But do not come back!"

Soon after, the bat fell down again – this time in front of the lair belonging to a weasel who hated birds.

"A bird at my house?" shrieked the weasel.

"I've a good mind to eat you up!" "B-but I am not a bird!" faltered the bat. "Otherwise I would have feathers on my wings! No, I am a mouse!"

The weasel came nearer, looking closely at the bat.

"All right!" she shouted at last. "Take yourself off! And in future, keep out of my sight!"

And so, the bat saved his skin. But he did it by changing his tune and bending the truth to suit himself.

People call this "double dealing". It is looked upon as being the same as telling lies.

8 The Fox, the Blackbird and the Good Boy

Melegari

Each day, a boy took a basket of food to his father, who worked in the fields. Fox wanted to get that basket! So he made a plan with the blackbird.

"Play your part," said Fox. "Then we'll meet under the green tree to share the food!" When the blackbird saw the boy coming, he flew down into the road, pretending to limp. "Poor blackbird!" said the boy. "Have you hurt yourself?" He put down the basket. "Let's see your claw!"

Whilst all this was going on, the sly old fox was gobbling up all the food! Soon, the boy was going home with an empty basket. The blackbird had an empty stomach. And the fox had a chicken bone stuck between his teeth! He found the blackbird by the big, green tree, and pointed to the bone, still firmly wedged in his mouth. The blackbird understood. But he turned away and went off... limping.

9 The Cat and the Mice

from Estonia

Do you know why cats and mice hate each other? Well, it all began many years ago, when the first tame cat made his master promise him a juicy beefsteak each day.

An agreement was written, stating that if there was no beefsteak, the cat's master would offer him a choice of lamb or veal, without bones.

Two copies were made – one for the man, one for the cat. The man put his copy in a drawer. The cat pinned his on a wooden beam in the barn where he slept, so that he could see it every morning as soon as he opened his eyes.

Then, one night, the mice (who chewed EVERYTHING), nibbled away at the paper until it was nothing but white powder!

Once the man knew what had happened, if the cat wanted beefsteak, he had to steal it! But – maybe he quite enjoyed chasing the mice, anyway!

10 How Fox paid his fare!

from Algeria

A fox asked a boatman to take him across a river. "What about the fare?" asked the man.

"Let us strike a bargain!" said the fox. "I shall tell you three things. You say if each one is true or false – and you will be paid!"

"Right!" said the man, thinking himself clever enough for a fox! "You can get in!"

"True or false?" said the fox, as the boat moved off. "A sausage in a roll is better than a roll in a sausage!"

"TRUE!" the man grinned. "True or false?" the fox went on. "When you hear people say – "What a beautiful night! It's as clear as day!" – that is not true. You can see better by day !"

"THAT's true!" said the boatman, pleased with himself. "What's the third question?"

"True or false?" said the fox. "It is nearly mid-day, and you are feeling hungry!" And out he jumped on to the bank!

"Hey!" shouted the boatman. "What about my fare?"

"I said I would tell you three things," Fox reminded him, "And you would say if they were true or false! Then you would be paid!"

"But I DID tell you whether they were true or false!" the man protested.

"Exactly!" said the fox. "And so you have been paid!"

"Aaaargh!" raged the boatman, and threw an oar at the fox. And the fox? He simply ducked his head and disappeared through the trees!

11 The Millipede and the Grasshopper

Fay

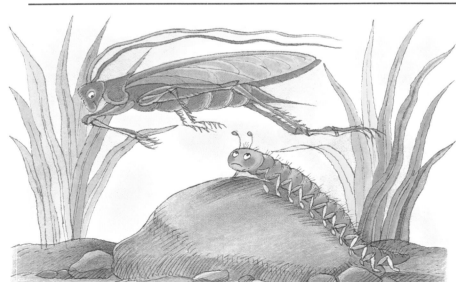

A millipede had to climb over a stone. "Phew!" he gasped. "What a mountain!"

Grasshopper laughed. "A stone may seem a mountain to you!" he said. "But not to me!"

And with a great jump, he leapt over the stone – still with the millipede on top!

And just like the millipede, some people make small jobs seem huge, difficult tasks.

12 The Anteater and the Jaguar

Melegari

"Father," said a young anteater, "why do we always eat ants?"

"Because we don't have any teeth!" said his father.

The anteater went to see the jaguar. "If only I had teeth!" he sighed. "Will you give me one of yours?"

"Certainly!" roared Jaguar. "Which one do you want?" He opened his mouth, the anteater came closer … and was gobbled up at once!

13 The Butterfly and the Violet

Trilussa

One day, attracted by a lovely scent, a butterfly flew into a wood. Down it fluttered between some bushes – and there in the shade, was a sweet-smelling violet, looking so meek and shy.

But, as the butterfly settled on one of the petals, the violet cried out, "Hey! Mind those feet of yours! I am the most delicate flower in the world! Sweethearts give me to their loved ones!

People put me between the pages of a book in remembrance! I am a sign –"

"A sign of what?" the butterfly managed to break in.

"A sign of shyness!" said the violet. "A sign of modesty! Shy people are often called "shrinking violets"!"

"Well," said the butterfly at last. "It seems to me that you are far from being shy! Or modest!"

And before the violet could say anything more, away it fluttered towards a field of cauliflowers.

14 The Tears of a Crocodile

Florian

Two goats had been drinking at a river, when one of them was eaten by a crocodile.

As the other goat ran off, the crocodile began to cry.

"That's it! Cry!" said the camel. "You do well to think about all your wrong-doing!"

"I am crying," sniffed the crocodile, "because I did not get the other goat!"

Crocodile tears are always false.

15 The All-Eating Raven

from Somalia

Long, long ago, all the birds of the world met to decide which of them would eat grain and which would feed on meat.

The raven's CAW-CAW! was heard loudest of all. "The birds who are smaller than me can eat seeds and berries! Those who are bigger than me can eat meat!"

"Agreed!" cried the others. And so it is that the raven eats both grain and meat!

16 Peke, the Pekingese

Melegari

Can you guess which is the question everyone asks Peke, the Pekingese puppy, when they meet him for the first time?

It's – "Are you really from Peking, the capital of China?"

Peke's owners had often told him how the history of the Pekingese dog which we know today goes back to 1861, when Queen Victoria was on the British throne.

This was the year when some loyal British subjects presented Her Majesty with the male and female of a breed of dog which they had developed in China.

At first, Peke was very interested and proud of his history.

But after passing on the same facts over and over again, he got tired of repeating himself.

So now, when new friends ask him, "Are you really from Peking?" he answers, "No! Just outside!"

17 The Cricket and the Butterfly

Florian

A black cricket was watching a butterfly. "How beautiful it is!" thought the cricket. "What lovely wings! Me, I am so plain! Nobody bothers to look at me!"

Some boys began chasing the butterfly and the cricket went into its hole, feeling sad for the lovely creature. "At least I live in peace," it thought. "So maybe it is sometimes best not to be noticed!"

18 The Singing Cockerel

Gesta Romanorum

There was once a cockerel who had such a beautiful voice that his master was very proud of him. Then, one day a fox pounced on the cockerel and carried him off in his mouth!

"Get that fox!" the owner of the cockerel commanded his dogs. "Get him!"

The cockerel was still held between the teeth of the fox. But he managed to crow back at the dogs, "No! Stay where you are!"

"That man was a terrible master!" the cockerel told the fox. "I wish you'd tell him to stay away, too!"

Fox did not think twice! "Yes!" he shouted to the owner of the cockerel. "You stay there!" Of course, as soon as he opened his mouth, the cockerel was free! Next moment, the bird had flown into a tree! Then he let forth a series of chirps and crows – just as if he were laughing at the fox!

19 The Donkey who pretended to be lame

Aesop

A donkey was grazing in a field when he saw a wolf coming. "Aihee!" brayed the donkey. He moved a few steps, pretending to be lame. "Help me, Wolf! I've got a thorn in my foot!"

The wolf growled under his breath. If he ate this donkey, he thought, that thorn could well stick in his mouth!

As if he had read the wolf's mind, the donkey lifted a rear hoof. "Perhaps you could help get the thorn out?" he brayed.

The wolf came nearer, his eyes on the raised hoof. Next minute, he felt a hard kick on his nose, and down he went!

"What a life!" he gasped, trying to clear his head. "My father taught me all he knew, and all I get for my trouble is a sore face and some loose teeth!" He sighed.

"It's true what people say. Those who take on a job for which they are not prepared must expect things to go wrong!"

20 The Porcupine and the ball of wool

from Romania

Mother Nature was trying to work out the best way to change from daylight to night-time on Earth. "I shall make some white yarn for the daylight hours," she decided at last, "and black yarn for the night. Someone can roll them together in a big ball, and then unroll it again, winding the white yarn on to one reel, then the black yarn on to another!"

She called a porcupine, an animal noted for its patience. The porcupine was given two reels of yarn – one white for the daylight hours, the other black for night-time hours – and so the work began.

No one knows how long it took the poor animal to wind the thread together into one great ball. But at last, it was finished.

Then the porcupine began re-winding the thread on to two reels, first the black yarn, then the white. But what a boring job it was – so boring that the porcupine dozed off! His right paw went on winding the black thread. But his left paw stopped completely – which meant that on Earth it was night all the time.

But all living things need the sun, otherwise they die...

At last, when the porcupine awoke and saw the disaster which he had caused, his spikes stood up in fear.

And to this day, when a porcupine is frightened, its spikes stand up on its back.

Then it looks just like a big ball of black and white wool.

21 The Anteater and his reflection

Melegari

An anteater went down to the river to have a drink – and saw his reflection in the water!

"Another anteater?" he cried. "Maybe he is bathing... It is rather warm...." Two days later, he went to drink at the same spot. "Why are you here again?" he grunted. "There aren't any ants in the river!"

"I know!" came the reply. "But I like a bit of peace!"

22 At the Court of the Lion

de la Fontaine

The lion, king of the animals, called all his subjects to his court – a big cave, where bones and bits of food gave off a horrible smell.

When the bear, who lived in the pure mountain air, held his nose in disgust, the lion knocked him down with one blow. "Bravo!" cried the monkey. "Our king's palace smells as sweet as any flower!"

The lion knew this was not true. He put out another paw and knocked the monkey down. "I want the truth!" he roared. "Is there a terrible smell here?" he asked the fox. "Or is it fresh and clean?"

"I'b afraid I hab a bat colt," sniffed the fox. "So I caddot smell a think! If Your Majesty says the air is clear, den I believe it!"

The lion did not like the blunt honesty of the bear. He hated the false flattery of the monkey. But the fox avoided the truth with tact. And so the lion spared him.

23 The Pear Tree and the Swallow

Novaro

This story is about an old pear tree. (Many pear trees are old – did you know it can take a pear tree up to eighty years to bear real fruit?)

Well, this tree was in the middle of a garden, all dry and wrinkled, in the grip of winter. Month after month it slept, through the snow and the rain, lashed by the north wind and sodden by puddles of icy cold water.

"The old pear tree will not wake again!" said the little blades of grass clustered around its roots. Then, early one spring morning, a swallow returning to its nest let out a little cry of joy.

Suddenly, the old pear tree seemed to shake itself, as if it were coming to life again after its long winter sleep.

The little cry of the swallow had awoken the old tree. And as it looked around, it found itself covered in blossom!

24 The Moon and the Monkeys

from China

Some monkeys saw the moon reflected in the bottom of a well. Their leader grabbed the branch of a tree. "Hold my tail!" he told another monkey. "Then a third can hold your tail! We'll make a chain long enough to go down the well!"

But the branch broke, there was a big SPLASH! and the monkeys fell into the water. And how the moon laughed at them from the sky!

25 The Chicken and the Dog

Trilussa

One day, in the courtyard of a big, country estate, a chicken was scratching about, looking for worms. Suddenly, she found herself facing a big dog!

"My-my lord," she bleated, quaking with fear, "I am sorry to have disturbed you!" And she hurried away, her heart beating loud enough for the dog to hear.

Passing through the courtyard some days later, the chicken saw the big dog again.

This time, the dog had a collar around its neck. And it was tied up with a thick chain so that it could not move far from its kennel.

"Ah-ha!" clucked the chicken, puffing out her chest with pride. "So, you have been put on a chain! What a sight you look, you miserable creature!"

"Chained up or not," snarled the dog, showing his teeth, "I am always strong! But you will always be a coward!"

26 The Fat Thrushes and the Thin Thrushes

Faerno

Tired of pecking around in the woods, some thrushes went to eat grapes in a vineyard. Three returned, so plump and fat, that the others piped up, "Can we come with you next time?"

"No," said a fat thrush. "We may still be alive. But the rest were shot. Better to stay thin but safe in your own home than to get fat on someone else's land and be in danger!"

27 Wings for a little camel!

Melegari

"Father," said a little camel one day, "I want to fly!"

"That's what I have always wanted!" sighed his father. "But camels have never flown and they never will!"

"Well, I WANT to fly!" insisted the little camel. "And I SHALL fly!"

He collected feathers from chickens, turkeys and ostriches and made a pair of wings. Then he went up on a minaret (that is what a bell-tower is called in the countries where camels live) and spreading his wings, he took a deep breath and jumped. A whistle. A thump. And the camel's legs spread outwards on the ground.

It was some while before he could pick himself up. Then he ran home faster than he had ever done before.

It was only later that he found he had an upside-down letter "V" on his legs, where he had fallen – a mark which all camels have to this day.

28 The Hare and the Goats

Florian

The hare in this story always tried to help other animals. He thought he had friends – until the day he was chased by a pack of hounds, and none of them offered him shelter.

Tired and frightened, that poor hare somehow reached a patch of waste land where some goats lived.

Seeing the hounds in the distance, one of the goats jumped out from behind a bush and ran off into the wood, the hounds following behind. Then the goat made a wide turn and returned to the bushes. Out jumped a second goat, ready to run and wear out the hounds.

The two goats took it in turns, tiring the hounds until they left. "Thank you!" said the hare. "It seems I do not have many friends, but –"

"You do not need many friends," said the goats. "It is enough to have just one who is a true friend."

29 The Brave Parrot

from China

There was once a yellow parrot who lived among a thousand other squawking, gossipy, chattering parrots. So, one day he decided to go to a place where he could get some peace and quiet.

Soon, he met some turtle-doves. They sang so softly! And each morning, as they awoke, they would groom their feathers and fly off all together to find food and drink and to play.

The yellow parrot really enjoyed the peace and quiet. But after a while, he began to pine for his own country and decided to return. He thanked the kind turtle-doves, and flew off. But, as he began flying a last circle of farewell – he saw a puff of smoke. The wood had caught fire! The home of the turtle-doves was threatened by flames!

The yellow parrot dived into a lake, sucked up as much water as he could, then flew towards the fire!

He shook his beak, so that the drops of water fell on to the fire. Again and again, he did the same thing – until, at last, Mother Nature saw him.

"How did you hope to put out the fire by yourself?" she asked.

"I don't know," said the parrot. "But it was all I could do to help my friends!" Mother Nature was so moved by the words of the yellow parrot, she made a great shower of rain. And that put out the fire in less time than it takes to tell.

30 The Donkey and the Guitar

Fedro

Browsing around in a field, a donkey found a guitar! *"Pling-Plang!"* went the strings, as he plucked them with his hoof. "What a talent I have!" he brayed. "Lucky I was the one who found this guitar, because I can play it! Me, a humble donkey!"

What the donkey did not know is – in life it is not enough to have luck. You must work hard too!

The Wolf and his Three Hams

AT a time when Mr Wolf and Mr. Fox were on friendly terms, the wolf invited the fox to supper.

He set a place for the fox, and asked his wife to serve him a good meal.

But, as Mr. Fox sat down to eat, he could not help looking up at three beautiful, juicy-looking hams hanging from the ceiling.

"Aren't you afraid of being robbed, my dear Wolf?" said the fox. "Or that your friends will expect you to give some of the ham to them?"

"Rob me?" scoffed the wolf. "How could anyone rob me, with my wife and cubs always at home? As for giving it away – that is something I would never do!"

"Those hams will not be eaten by anyone except me!" the wolf continued, his voice dropping to a whisper. "Not even my wife or my children!"

"All the same," said the fox. "if I were you, I would hide those hams. Then you can spread the word that you HAVE been robbed! That way, you will be able to enjoy those hams in peace, just as you please!"

The wolf shrugged his shoulders. He did not think he needed advice!

"Thank you for the meal," said the fox, bolting down the last mouthful, "and good night to your family!" And with a bow to Mrs. Wolf and a wink at the cubs, he went out into the dark night.

But the fox did not go far – only just outside the wolf's house. Then, as the night grew darker and the deep snores of the wolf and his family could be heard, so Fox jumped up at the straw roof of the wolf's house. He scratched out a big hole, snatched the three hams and went back to his lair for another feast – this time with his wife and fox-cubs!

The night passed, the stars faded, the cockerel crowed – and the wolf opened his eyes to a new day.

And the first thing that he saw was the great big hole in his roof!

"Aaaargh!" he roared, trying

to see how the hole had got there. Then he noticed that his three lovely, juicy hams were missing!

The wolf gave such a yell, all the doors and windows burst open. Mrs. Wolf and the cubs woke up with a start.

"I've been robbed of my three hams!" groaned the wolf, tears in his eyes. He went to the door and looked up at the sky. "I have been robbed of my hams!" he shouted at a pink cloud floating by.

Just then, along came the fox,

keeping a safe distance from the angry wolf.

"I have been robbed of my hams!" the wolf roared again. Fox winked, one paw behind his ear, as if he had not heard. "What's that, my friend?"

"I have been robbed!" croaked the wolf. "I have been robbed!"

"You have been robbed?" echoed the fox, raising his voice so that the wolf had to shout even louder to make himself heard. "What has been taken?"

"My three hams!" wailed the wolf. "I've been robbed of my

three beautiful hams!"

"That's right!" hissed the fox. "Keep saying it so that everyone will hear! Good to see you taking my advice!"

"But I really HAVE been robbed!" yelled the wolf.

"You are a natural actor!" smiled the fox. "So believable!"

"There's a great, big hole in my roof!" shouted the wolf.

"What does that matter," said the fox, "compared to the joy of having saved your hams!"

"HE'S BEEN ROBBED OF THREE HAMS!" added the smallest wolf cub, with the others joining in, dancing in a circle. "HE'S BEEN ROBBED OF THREE HAMS!"

"That's enough!" roared the wolf in fury. "I am the ONLY one who says we have been robbed of three hams!"

"Oh – let them say it too," the fox put in. "Clever little things! They ARE the sons of a great actor, aren't they?"

And with the wolf quite unable to say another word, the fox moved off, mischief glinting in his eyes.

Gesta Romanorum

1 The Peacock and the Crane

Aesop

"See my lovely feathers!" said the peacock to the crane. "You always look so dull!"

"You may be more handsome than I," said the crane. "But I sing near the stars, and fly high into the sky! All you do is to strut around like a chicken!"

There was no reply. The crane had shown that we should be judged by what we do, not what we look like.

2 The Ant and the Grasshopper

Aesop

Ant had worked hard all summer, gathering grains of wheat, barley and maize to store in his ant-hill.

Now, it was winter. So he pulled the food out to dry a little in the pale sunshine.

"Please," came the voice of a hungry grasshopper, "will you give me a little food?"

"Why didn't you gather food during the summer?" asked the ant.

"But I was singing all summer long!" said the grasshopper. "That is what grasshoppers do! So, what time did I have to get food for the winter?"

"Well, my dear," said the ant, "after so much singing, now you can dance!" And he went away and left her there.

This fable has been told in many ways. But the meaning is always the same.

If you are lazy and do not stock up with something for the future, you have only yourself to blame if you are in want later on

3 The Puma, the Mouse and the Armadillo

Melegari

Puma had always wanted to eat an armadillo. But, as you may know, when there is danger, an armadillo rolls itself into a hard ball! So Puma got the help of a mouse. And when the armadillo went to roll into a ball, the mouse began tickling him until his body sprung open – bouncing the mouse into the puma's mouth! Trickery often backfires on the culprits!

4 The Parrot who became a Critic

Florian

There was once a parrot who escaped into a wood. And, because he was big and fat, with beautiful feathers and a loud voice, other birds began to see him as their leader, going to him for advice and guidance.

This made the parrot feel most important! What a clever bird he must be, he thought! Before long, he began giving his views just as he pleased.

He found fault with the nightingale's song – because she "dragged out the notes". The chaffinch sounded as if it had hiccups, and the song of the thrush was boring.

"Excuse me," the lapwing put in, "may we hear how you sing?"

"I do not sing!" answered the parrot haughtily. "I talk!"

The birds laughed and chased the parrot from the wood!

But, just like him, there are people who criticise the way others do something which they cannot do themselves.

5 The Monkey Gardeners

from India

Long ago in the grounds of a sultan's palace, a gardener heard music coming from the town square and wished he could be there. But there were hundreds of rose-beds still to be watered.

Then he saw the monkeys who were kept as pets of the sultan. Why not give them the job of watering the rose-beds? He went and asked the chief of the monkeys.

"Certainly!" said the monkey.

"Thank you!" cried the man. "Work just how you like!" And off he went.

"We'll do this job better than he does!" said the monkey. "He only sprinkled water at the bottom of the stem! We'll uproot each one – and those with a lot of roots will get two pails of water! The others, just one pail!"

And when the gardener returned later on, he learned that the jobs left to others are not always done as we want.

6 The Dog and the Motorway

Melegari

A little dog was running along the motorway. *"Braummm –!"* went a sports car, letting out a jet of hot exhaust, like a desert wind.

The little dog ran on and on, the ribbon of black, shiny asphalt seeming unending.

"Vroom!" went a dormobile. with a family inside. Still he ran on and on.

And still there was no end to the motorway.

"Broom-boom!" went a mini-car. This time, the dog could see a young couple inside, smiling at each other instead of looking at the road ahead. Still, he ran on and on. *"Brum-brum!"* went a caravan, full of rattling saucepans.

"Brum-brum!" went a container lorry, as big as a house.

Still the dog ran on and on. Abandoned at the side of the motorway, it was all he could do, until he reached the other end – and, who knows? – a kind person to give him a good home.

7 The Little Horse and the Donkey

Melegari

In the stables of a fine, big house a young horse lived with a donkey. The donkey was used to carry things which people in the house needed – apart from being ridden by the children. But the young horse was groomed carefully. Beautifully harnessed and decked with flowers, she was ridden by important people. And her manger was always full with sweet hay and oats.

"I do as much work as you, plus a lot more!" groaned the poor donkey, "yet look how much better you are treated! See how people admire you, with the elegant riders in your saddle! But who sees me, when I am only ridden around in circles?"

"I know," said the horse, "and I do not like to see it. But that is the way life goes. You are such a patient animal. And many think that patience means you should be content with things as they are."

8 The King of all the Deer

from China

The forest deer had a king who was very wise. He was also troubled by so many deer being killed by hunters. In the end, he went to see the emperor. "Your Majesty," said the deer, "your hunters have killed hundreds of my fellow creatures who live in your forests. It cannot go on!"

He took a deep breath. "How many deer do you need for food each day?"

"Just one," said the emperor. "Then that is what you shall have!" the deer decided. "And in return, I must ask you to stop killing the rest!"

So the king of the deer returned to his subjects to tell them of the agreement he had made with the emperor.

The deer knew that their king had acted for the best. Sooner or later, they told each other, they would have to die. So it made sense for one of them to be killed each day, to save the rest from danger.

But one day, it was the turn of a mother deer who had just had a fawn. She prayed her life would be spared, otherwise her baby would die too.

The king of the deer knew he had to keep to the agreement with the emperor. So he went to the emperor and offered himself. This action moved the emperor so much that he set the deer free. Even so, the idea of killing someone who had become a friend troubled him. So in the end, he passed a law that no more deer should be killed.

9 The Mosquito and the Bull

Fedro

A mosquito had dared a bull to fight him! The bull accepted – and on the day of the fight, all the animals gathered to watch the two contestants enter the arena.

The bull lowered his horns. But the mosquito said, "Thank you, Bull, for agreeing to fight a little one like me! Now I can say that I am as brave as you!" And he flew off, buzzing loudly.

10 A Sparrow, all alone

Amorth

A sparrow was bored, just pecking around. So he thought he would follow the swallows, flying off to warmer lands.

By the time they reached the sea, he was already tired. He managed to follow the swallows for a bit longer. But above the waves, his strength gave out, and he fell into the ocean.

Those who want too much sometimes lose all they have.

11 The Owl and the Pigeon

Florian

An owl was perched on a branch, looking so sad that a pigeon flew down beside him.

"What's wrong?" he asked.

"I'm old, sick and alone," said the owl. "Nobody talks to me or comes to see me..."

"Don't you have any children, family or friends?" asked the pigeon.

"Children? Pah!" snorted the owl. "Too much trouble to find a wife! Families are a bother, anyway. And don't talk to me about friends, either! I always say you cannot trust any of them!"

"But have you never wanted to be with anyone in your life?"

"Never!" snapped the old owl with a loud, angry hoot.

"Well," said the pigeon, "no wonder you are always on your own and nobody talks to you! Why are you feeling sorry for yourself?"

And away he flew, as fast as he could.

12 The Fox and the Cricket

Aesop

A cricket sat on a high branch of an olive tree, singing in the summer sun. "What a lovely song!" cried the fox. He had just finished eating a cockerel. A cricket, he thought, would make a nice dessert! "Come a bit lower, so I can hear it more clearly!"

But the cricket brushed down a leaf, and the fox ate that!

Then the cricket started singing again!

13 The Tail of the Fox

Afanasjev

A fox fled into a hole to escape a pack of hounds.

"My dear eyes," he said, "what are you doing as I run from the hounds?"

"We look at the ground," said his eyes, "so that you do not trip or tread on a stone!"

"And you, my ears?" asked the fox. "What are you doing?"

"Listening out to hear which way the hounds are coming!" replied his ears.

"And you, tail," the fox went on, "what are you doing?"

"I am just left behind!" said the tail. "And I am tired of being last in the hole!"

"That!" said the fox, "seems very unfair!" And he put his tail outside the hole, waving it like a flag. "Hounds!" he shouted. "Eat my tail!"

The hounds ran up, bit into the tail – and then the fox.

An old proverb says that once a tail is lost, everything else is lost, too.

14 The Snail and the Rose Bed

Lorenzoni

"What lovely sunshine!" sang a little rose tree. "The whole world seems to be at play!"

"If it is at play for you," said a snail, poking his head out of its hole, "why can't it be at play for me?" So he came out and began to explore.

He could see the branches of the rose tree, covered by thorns, the garden path and the washing hung out to dry. But the sun seemed a long way off. Perhaps would see it better if he climbed the wall?

Now, in front of the garden wall, there was a lawn, trimmed and kept neat and tidy by the man who lived in the house. As you can guess, he did not like a snail crawling over it to get to the wall! He picked up the snail on his spade and hurled it away.

When it recovered, the snail found itself back outside his hole! Safe inside once again, he poked his head out and said to the rose tree, "That's the last time I listen to you!"

15 The Pike with a thousand teeth

Afanasjev

Every pike is a very greedy fish. But there was one pike who was the greediest of all. This pike was small and fat, but he ate like a wolf. And he was strong, with a thousand teeth! Barbel fish, carp, perch, tench…. he gobbled them all! And he grew and grew – not day by day, but hour by hour!

Terrified, the other fish left the river. So the pike with a thousand teeth began to feed on freshwater prawns.

And when he had eaten all he could find, he went hunting for worms – and that was his downfall. One worm was so big and fat, it hid the fisherman's hook, from which it hung.

Seeing such a nice, big, fat juicy worm, the pike with a thousand teeth opened his mouth… He was so heavy, the fisherman almost dropped his rod – almost, but not quite! Before very long, that pike with a thousand teeth finished up in the cooking pot!

16 The Wasps, the Partridges and the Man

Aesop

One hot summer's day, the wasps and the partridges went and asked a man for a drink. "Give us some water," said the partridges, "and we will help you clean the vineyard!"

"And if anyone ever tries to rob you," said the wasps, "we shall sting them!"

"Well," said the man, "I do not have much water. And there are my two oxen…"

"Of course!" buzzed the wasps. "Such hard-working animals must not go thirsty!" added the partridges.

"Yes," said the man. "My oxen are hard-working. But they do not make any promises! Instead they do all that I ask! It seems best that they should drink the water I have, not you!"

This story is told to show that it is best to trust those who prove their worth by hard work and honest toil, rather than those who make wild promises which they may not be able to keep.

17 The Stag who thought he was ugly

Lessing

There was once a deer who, because he was a little bigger and stronger than the others and had a thicker neck, felt very ashamed and awkward. So, he tried to make everyone think that he was an elk.

Now an elk is more than two metres high. And because of its great antlers which can weigh up to 20 kilos, it always walks with its head down. It has long ears like a donkey and makes a noise like a cow.

When an elk gets in a bad mood, its muzzle, large and flat like a boxer's nose, almost touches the ground. Its eyes get small and dark, and it makes such a dismal, howling sound.

So – what was there for a stag to make people think he was an elk? Nothing.

Just like that stag, there are people who try to pretend to be someone different and make themselves look ridiculous.

18 The Swallow and the Flax

Fedro

A swallow saw a flax plant, from which we get linen, growing in a field. "People make threads from the fibres of that plant to make nets!" he cried. "In those nets, they catch birds like us!"

The other birds laughed and flew down to nest under the roofs of houses. They were safe. But birds have been caught in nets for centuries. And they are still being caught today.

19 The Lion and the Hare

Eliano

The crowing of a cockerel is famous. But it is a sound which, according to ancient legend, can frighten a lion!

One day, a hare wanted to find out if this tale was true. So he went to the lion. "Your Majesty," he began, "it is said that the shrill song of the cockerel makes you flee – you, the strong, unbeatable lion! Can it be true?"

"It is!" the lion answered at once. "All of us have weaknesses, even the strongest lion!"

The hare could only stand there with his mouth open! "Haven't you heard how the largest elephant will run away from the smallest mouse?" the lion went on. "And that asses become frightened as soon as the grunting of pigs reaches their long but delicate ears?"

"Oh!" The hare gave a smile. "Now I understand why hares run away in fright when they hear a dog barking!"

20 The Lion and the Long-Eared Owl

Melegari

When Nature was still deciding what each animal should be like, Lion was already a good runner and jumper – until he fell into a deep hole.

And there he would have stayed, if the long-eared owl had not seen him and called the other animals to help. Nature rewarded this owl by giving it feathers the colour of the lion and drawing a ring of silver around its eyes.

21 The Wolf and the Little Goats again

Afanasjev

Remember the story of how a wolf tried getting into the the little goats' cottage? He pretended he was Mother Goat – but when he forgot the words of her song, they knew it was the wolf trying to trick them!

But the wolf did not give up. He tried to copy the song of the nightingale, then the parrot's voice... and before long, he was at their cottage once more.

"Little goats," he began, in a strange-sounding voice. "Will you open the door?"

Quite forgetting the wolf, the goats opened the door, and – gobble-gobble! – he ate them up! Feeling very full, he set off home, not seeing a hole where a woodcutter had lit a fire to cook some broth. The wolf fell inside and finished up as a red-hot cinder! The heat made his stomach burst open – and out came the little kids! They ran back to their mother, knowing that they did not have to fear the wolf any longer.

22 The Partridge and the Fox

Fedro

"Such beautiful pink feet you have, partridge!" said a fox one day. "And I hear you also have pink eyelids! May I see?"

The partridge closed its eyes, and – *zump!* – the fox seized it.

"Please," said the partridge, "let me hear your lovely voice say my name one last time!"

"Partridge –" the fox began. He had barely said the word, before the bird flew away!

23 The Storyteller who went to Heaven

Melegari

We all know that the souls of good people go to Heaven when they die. But, what about animals and birds? Is there just one of each creature? Or do the souls of all the dogs – past, present and future – all the kangaroos, fleas, cockroaches, insects and so on, go to Heaven, too?

Well, there was once a storyteller who made up his mind that he would find out when he got to Heaven! The first creatures he saw there were all the hundreds and thousands of foxes who had died over the centuries! "So you are a storyteller!" said one. "Then maybe you can tell us why we are always written about as cheats, plotters, gossips, liars and killers?"

The storyteller could give no reply. In all the stories which are told about Heaven, there are many questions which cannot be answered.

24 The Goose who laid the Golden Eggs

Aesop

There was once a man who had a hen which laid an egg of solid gold each morning! He had been poor before he got the hen. But as he got richer, so he began getting greedy.

Suppose, he thought, he were to discover the hen's secret? He could get other hens, and turkeys to lay golden eggs! Or, what about the huge eggs of an ostrich? A golden egg that size would be worth a fortune!

"What's the secret?" the man demanded. The hen said nothing. "Tell me!" shouted the man. "Or, else!" And he twisted his hands together, as if he would wring the neck of the poor hen.

He repeated the question again and again. But the hen was too scared to answer. Losing patience, he killed that poor little hen. But when he opened her up, he found she was the same as any other hen.

And that was the end, not only of the pretty little hen, but of the golden eggs, too.

25 The Fox and the Butter

Aesop

One day, a fox frightened a hen in the farmyard, making her squawk so loudly that a milkmaid who had been making butter in the dairy came out.

The fox darted inside and licked all the butter! When the milkmaid discovered what had happened, she flung a vat of butter at him. And from that day to this, all foxes have a white tip on their tails.

26 The Hare in Disguise

from Africa

Hare had played so many tricks on Hippopotamus and Elephant, they decided to punish him.

"I will look for him in the forest," said the elephant. "You look around the swamp!"

But when Elephant saw Hare, he did not know it was him – because Hare wore a fawn's skin which he had found, and spoke just like a baby deer.

"I am looking for Hare!" the elephant began.

"Him!" snorted Hare. "When I wouldn't lend him something, do you know what he did? He spat at me!"

"Disgusting!" Elephant burst out. But before he could say any more, Hare scampered off towards the swamp, where he came across Hippopotamus.

"I am looking for Hare!" said the hippopotamus, thinking he was talking to a baby deer.

"Him!" snorted the hare. "When I asked for something I lent him – do you know what he did? He spat at me!"

Then Hare disappeared into a bush, took off the fawn's skin and waited until Elephant arrived before he came out. "Just who we want to see!" burst out Hippopotamus and Elephant.

"Looking for trouble?" said Hare. "Let me do to you what I did to that rude little fawn!"

Hippopotamus and Elephant looked at each other. "NO!" they both shouted. And as Elephant lumbered away, Hippopotamus hid beneath the water!

Brains often beat strength!

27 The Jackal and the Lion

from Asia

Jackal followed a lion, waiting to eat the left-overs from the lion's prey – as jackals do.

"Lion's roar tells everyone how big and strong he is!" thought Jackal. "If I roar, everyone will think the same about me!" So he tried to roar like the lion. "Aaaargh!" Nobody took any notice. But whilst he wasted time in stupid pretence, vultures had eaten his meat.

28 The Wild Boar and the Sheep

Gay

A lamb was tied up, ready to go to the slaughter-house, whilst the rest of the flock could only watch, trembling. "It's your own fault if you're frightened!" grunted a wild boar. "For centuries men have sheared you and used your wool, eaten your meat and stained their hands with your blood. Yet you do nothing, except tremble and wait for your turn to be killed!"

"We may look calm and patient," interrupted the ram. "But we do know how to get our own back!"

"How?" sneered the wild boar.

"You have feet which can kill and injure," the ram went on. "But we have skins from which parchments are made. For centuries, punishments have been written on those parchments! And with our skins, men make drums which call to soldiers to battle, where men are killed who kill animals. And all that is our silent revenge!"

29 The Nightjar in the Tree

Melegari

Like owls, a nightjar goes hunting for small animals at night. It sits quite still and ruffles a feather, sounding like a dry branch rustling in the night air. Then, as soon as a prey comes in sight – *zap!* – it swoops down!

One night, a nightjar was about to swoop down on a grass snake, when – *toc! tic! toc!* – along came a woodpecker who thought it was on a real branch!

30 The Horse and the Car

Melegari

These days, we see fewer horses and more and more cars. To see horses in the flesh, most people would have to go somewhere like a race-course or a Horse Show. Knowing this, one particular little car never could resist poking fun at the horse. "You on your four feet can't go half as far as I can on my four wheels!" said the car. "Why, my engine has the power of twenty horses! I can carry four people, whilst you only have one saddle! And I can go much quicker and faster! These days, vehicles like me do all that horses once did, and a lot more besides!" The horse said nothing. It stretched its head, made two wide turns around the car, ran forward – and leaped over the car.

The car could only stay there, its bonnet gaping open in amazement!

"Now," neighed the horse, "you try jumping over me!"

31 The Woodland String Quartet

Krylov

In a string quartet, two musicians play violins, one plays viola and one a cello.

The music is lovely – except when the musicians are a bear, a monkey, a goat and a donkey – as they are in this story!

They thought they would put on a concert! But instead of music, there seemed to be only scratching and scraping!

"Let us change places!" the monkey said at last. "Bear, bring your cello alongside me, as first violin! You Donkey, with your viola, sit beside Goat, who is the second violin!" But, if anything, they sounded even worse! Just then, a nightingale came flying overhead.

"To be good musicians, you need more than instruments and music!" she said. "It takes a good ear, and years of study, practice and hard work!" And she began singing a beautiful song – just to prove to the animals that she knew what she was talking about.

The Hare
and the Tortoise

ONE lovely summer's day, the woodland animals met beneath a great oak tree to have a chat.

There was the fox – cunning, vain, but very clever. The owl with its fine eyesight. The stag, proud of his splendid antlers. The mole, an expert at digging. And – the hare.

"When it comes to running," he was saying, "there is no one to beat me! To us hares, speed is an art, a great talent! Imagine how I felt when I got a thorn in my paw and could only go as fast as the tortoise! The shame of it!"

"What cheek!" cried the tortoise, peeping out of his shell. "I know I am not a champion of speed! But I can keep going well enough!"

"Come on, Tortoise!" said the fox. "You must agree that when it comes to running, you don't stand a chance!"

"That's not true!" stormed the tortoise. "I can use my feet when I have to!"

"Oh, stop arguing!" said the stag. "Look, why not let the hare and the tortoise have a race?"

"Good idea!" cried Badger. "They can race from here to the bottom of the valley!"

"That suits me!" said the tortoise at once. "What about you, Hare?"

"I'm not sure if it is quite fair to a slowcoach like you," murmured Hare, stroking his whiskers. "But just to show what a good runner I am, I accept!"

"Right!" said the fox. "Now, stand side by side, and wait for my signal! Ready, steady... go!"

The hare shot off at once, raising a cloud of dust. Only after this settled could the animals see the tortoise, struggling along as best he could.

"Now they'll see what I can do!" Hare was thinking. "I'll make mincemeat of that tortoise! Talking of mincemeat – I am feeling a bit hungry.." By this time, the hare was approaching a farm. Surely, he thought, he had time for a little snack!

The farm animals were pleased to see him.

"Hello, Hare!" lowed the

cows. "How are you?"

"How is the running career?" crowed the cockerel.

"What are you doing here?" asked the rabbits.

Hare bit into a juicy radish. "I am supposed to be running against Tortoise!" he giggled. "He challenged me to a race!"

"He must be crazy!" bleated the goat. "Where is he, now?"

"Still back at the starting point, I should think!" laughed the hare, now enjoying a fat, red carrot. "I've still got plenty of time for an after-dinner nap under the nut tree before he gets anywhere!"

And soon, the hare was making himself comfortable in the shade of the tree. He closed his eyes, crossed his legs – and began snoring.

As for the poor tortoise, he was trudging along, tongue hanging out and gasping for breath as he began climbing the hill which would lead down to the valley.

He came to the farm, and when he saw Hare, still asleep, he gave a little smile... By the time Hare opened his eyes, it was almost sunset! He had slept much longer than he meant to!

He jumped to his feet, and shot off like an arrow.

How the hare ran! Plants, trees, animals, fields... he passed them all in a flash, before stepping over stones in a stream, jumping down on to the other bank, and running on.

Suddenly, his long ears heard voices in the distance.

"Hurrah!" the animals were shouting. "Well done!"

"Fancy that!" thought the Hare. "They're cheering me already!"

But when Hare came in sight of the finishing post, he saw the animals carrying the tortoise shoulder-high!

Tortoise looked truly worn out. But he was smiling. He had won the race!

And the moral of this story is – natural talent is not enough. You need to undertake a task carefully, in order to get the result which you want.

de la Fontaine

1 The Spider and the pain in the ankle

Gozzi

The spider is often treated as a nuisance, especially by town-dwellers.

The same goes for a pain in the ankle, both in the country and in the town.

One spider chose to live in the town house of a rich man.

"Such big rooms!" it thought. "I can spin my webs in peace!"

The pain in the ankle chose the foot of a poor peasant man.

"In the country," it thought, "there are not so many doctors or nurses! So I can stay here in peace!"

But the spider often had its webs destroyed by maids with long brooms, whose job it was to sweep spiders' webs from every corner.

The pain in the ankle was not much luckier.

True, the peasant found it troublesome – but the pain did not stop him digging the ground, collecting wood or picking peas at the right time.

"Suppose we change places?" suggested the spider.

So the spider moved into the peasant's house and settled in the kitchen. And the pain in the ankle went to the foot of the rich man. The foot was placed on silk cushions, rubbed with sweet-smelling ointment and carefully massaged.

And the spider had never been so happy, catching lots of flies in the peasant's kitchen!

Which just goes to show – what may not suit one, often suits another!

2 The Raven and the Eagle

de la Fontaine

A raven watched an eagle sink its claws into the thick wool of a lamb and carry it off.

"Suppose I do the same?" the raven thought, diving on to a sheep. But the sheep was too heavy to lift! Even worse, the raven could not get his claws out of the sheep's wool!

Later, the shepherd put the raven in a cage to think how stupid it was to try something which was clearly impossible.

June

3 The Heron and the Crane

Afanasjev

A heron and a crane lived at opposite sides of a swamp. The heron decided that he wanted to marry the crane. So he flew across the swamp and asked her.

"No!" she said. "I shall never marry a bean-pole like you!"

But once the heron had flown back across the swamp, she thought, "I may always be alone if I do not marry Heron."

So, she flew all the way across the swamp to the heron. "I will marry you!" she said.

"A wife who scratches the mud with her beak?" sneered the heron. "No, thank you!"

And so the crane flew all the way back across the swamp. But the heron was sorry he had spoken so harshly. So, he flew across the swamp and asked the crane to marry him.

"No!" she said. "I do not want a husband with long, red legs!" And so it went on. But, this story must end, with the thought that it is not only people who cannot make up their minds.

4 The Poet and the Snail

Cozzani

A poet's eye takes notice of everything. That is how they find things to write about.

One day, a poet was looking at the eyes of a snail. "How is it," said this poet, "that you have these strange eyes on top of your horns?"

"Strange?" said the snail. "With these eyes, I do the same as you when you point a telescope at the sky!"

"By day," the snail went on, "I see the wings of birds and butterflies in the sky. And in the deep blue of the night, I watch the stars going around the moon! I see them fading, until it is daybreak. Then I know they have gone to sleep."

"And do you miss them?" asked the poet.

"No," smiled the snail. "I look around and see more stars in the shapes of roses, lilies and violets!"

"Thank you!" said the poet. "I can write a lovely poem, now!"

5 The Fox and the Peasant

Melegari

"Please come down and read me a letter which has been sent to all the woodland animals!" Fox asked a pheasant sitting in a tree. "I cannot see too well!"

"My eyesight is the same as yours!" cried the pheasant. "But I can see a hunter coming along with a long rifle!"

The fox ran off – and the pheasant laughed so much, it nearly fell off the branch!

6 The Mosquito and the Spider

Melegari

After stinging and stinging all night long, Mosquito was very tired by morning! So he settled on a wall, hoping he would not be seen, and was then squashed with a blow from a slipper!

Later on, the same mosquito was buzzing around, when he saw a spider spinning its web.

"Is it true," he said, wanting to show how clever he was, "that your web is soft and very sticky?"

"Rubbish!" laughed the spider. "If my web were soft and sticky, how could I jump up and down on it, like children do on springy beds? Look, it's lovely and bouncy!" And to prove what he said, the spider jumped two or three times on the web.

"Ooh!" cried the mosquito. "Can I have a go?"

"Of course!" said the spider.

The mosquito jumped on to the web – closed his wings, his eyes... and was no more.

7 The Magpie and the Doves

Florian

A pair of peaceful doves had a nest next to some quarrelsome magpies. The magpie hen often complained about her husband. "Try not to be too touchy!" the dove hen said one day.

"I'm not touchy!" screamed the magpie. "I only came to tell you about my husband!"

So you see – it is hard to see our own faults as well as those of others!

8 The Nightingale and her rivals

Pascoli

A nightingale was singing and singing, each note like the ripple of water in a stream. Suddenly, another song, loud and strong, drowned hers out! *Cuckoo! Cuckoo!*

The nightingale fell silent, thinking hard. After that, her song was heard only at night, a song to suit the twilight and the splendour of the stars, a song of thanks for the beauty of the world around her.

Then one night, a loud *"Whoo-Whoo!"* interrupted her song. It was the horned owl, a bird who comes out at night.

After more thought, the nightingale gave the owl the honour of being the songbird of darkness. Then she flew off, her song mingling with the soft splash of water in a fountain and the murmur of leaves in the cypress tree. The wise nightingale had learned that at times someone else can do something better than you.

9 The Wolf and the Heron

Aesop

The wolf had a sheep bone stuck firmly in his throat. And the only creature he could see to help was a heron.

"I – I've g-got a b-bone... st-tuck in m-my throat!" croaked the wolf.

"Open your mouth!" ordered the heron.

"Aaaaargh!" went the wolf. The heron put his head right down between the wolf's wide-open jaws, caught the bone in his long, sharp beak and pulled it out. The wolf gave a big gulp to clear his throat. Then he turned away.

"Hey!" screeched the heron. "What about a reward?"

"Huh!" sniggered the wolf. "You have just taken your head from the mouth of the wolf, and you want another reward?"

And away he went without another word, leaving the heron thinking how foolish it is to expect any thanks from selfish creatures.

10 The Mullet and the Clam

Melegari

Some people wave to attract attention. A mullet swimming in the sea waved his fins for the same reason. "Nobody will notice you!" he told a clam. "You're always closed up!"

Soon after, the mullet and the clam were served in a meal. "My favourite!" said a man, spooning up the clam. But the mullet was eaten without anyone saying a word..

11 The Mice and the Weasels

Aesop

The mice and the weasels had been at war for a long time. And after so many mice had been killed in battle, the rest decided to form a proper army, with a commander in charge of each unit.

The new commanders were very proud of themselves! They wanted something to show that they were in charge. So, they each put on a helmet with a face-guard and a pair of horns.

How stupid they were! Such a show of pride served no useful purpose. And when it came to the next battle, the mice were once again put to flight by the weasels.

The ordinary mice were able to get back to their holes quickly. But those vain commanders were easily seen by the enemy. Not being able to enter their holes because of their helmets with the face-guards and tall horns, these mice commanders soon became victims of the weasels.

12 The Donkey and the Puppy

Fedro

A man loved his puppy so much that the donkey thought perhaps he should be more like the little dog.But when he greeted the man by putting his hooves on his shoulders and trying to lick him, just as the puppy did, the man got annoyed.

"I was silly to try and copy someone else," thought the donkey. "It only got me into trouble!"

13 The Hare and the Crocodiles

from Japan

Do you know why the hare has such a short tail? The story begins when he lived on a beautiful island where there were lots of flowers and little woods, the air ruffling his long ears and his tail – which at that time was long, rather like the tail of a fox.

Across the water, the hare could see some land. And before long, he thought of an idea how he could get there.

He went to the crocodiles. "Do you think," he said, "there are more crocodiles in the world, or hares?"

"More crocodiles!" they answered at once.

"And I say there are more hares!" said Hare. "So, why don't we count! You line up in the water between the island and that land over there," he went on. "Then I'll jump over your backs, counting as I go! Then we'll count the hares!"

"Right!" croaked the crocodiles. And, tail to nose, they laid across the water.

"One, two, three.." he began, hopping from one crocodile to the other. "Twenty.. Thirty.. One hundred.. Two hundred.." And as he got to the last one, he shouted back, "Thanks, you lizard-skins! Now try counting the hares!"

With a burst of laughter, he made a jump for the land.

But the last crocodile caught the hare by his tail, and *snap-snap* left him with only the stump of a tail!

So, now you know..

14 The Dog who saw justice done

Pulci

Remember the wolf who fell down a well when a fox tricked him? The fox was still laughing when he told a dog the whole story. "That wolf's face!" he chortled. "I should be famous!"

"You betrayed someone's trust, pretending to be his friend!" growled the dog. "Nobody takes kindly to that!" And he gave that fox the thrashing he deserved.

15 The Donkey's skin

Aesop

Once upon a time there was a donkey who belonged to a band of travelling performers. So often the poor donkey was beaten and loaded up until he could hardly stand. In the end, he died.

After that, the performers had to carry everything. Soon, they met another concert party.

"Where is the donkey?" asked their friends.

"He's dead!" came the answer.

"So," said one, "do you beat each other, now?"

"No," said the head of the company. "He takes all the beatings!"

"He?" questioned another. "Who's he?"

"The donkey!" said the man. "We used his skin to re-cover our drums. The blows which he took during his life sound much better now!"

It is true what many people say. So often, there is no respect for the loyal, hard-working animal.

16 The Goat and the Wolves

Afanasjev

Nanny Goat was tired of being on a farm. So she talked Billy Goat into going away to live in the wild.

Before they went, she took down the skin of a wolf from the shed door. The farmer had pinned it up as a hunting trophy some time ago. Nanny Goat put the skin in a bag and off she and Billy Goat went into the cold, dark night.

In the middle of a cold, dark wood, they came to a clearing, lit up by a fire. A cook-pot hung over it, and a pack of wolves sat around, warming themselves and waiting for something hot to eat!

"Greetings, brother wolves!" Nanny Goat cried. Behind her, Billy Goat shivered, and not only from the cold! "Would you like to share your meal with us?"

And she took the wolf's skin from her bag, dragging it along by the tail. Seeing this, the wolves ran away in fright – leaving Nanny and Billy Goat to the fire and a big feed!

17 The Ass and the Salt

Aesop

One day, an ass was going along weighed down by two enormous sacks of salt.

He came to a stream – but still he plodded on. Halfway across, the ass stumbled and fell. When he got to his feet, he was surprised to find that the sacks weighed much less!

Of course, the salt had dissolved in the water – but the ass thought it was the water which had made the bags so much lighter!

Some days later, the same ass came to the stream again – but this time, he was carrying sponges.

When he pretended to stumble, as he had before, he found himself up to his neck in the river – the sponges had soaked up so much water! The ass could not pick himself up!

So, you see, if we try making short cuts when we do something, we may only be making things worse for ourselves.

18 The Fox and the Stork

de la Fontaine

One day, the fox invited the stork to lunch. But all he offered was broth, served up in plates. The poor old stork could only get the tip of its beak into the plate, whilst the fox lapped up everything in a matter of minutes!

The fox thought it a huge joke. But the stork did not like it one bit. "You just wait!" he thought, seeing the fox trying not to laugh.

Well, a few days later, the stork returned the invitation. It so happened that the fox had not eaten that day, so, he was feeling very hungry by the time he arrived.

"Something smells good!" he said. "What is it?"

"Stew!" the stork announced proudly. And he served it up in a vase with a long, thin neck! All the fox could enjoy was the smell!

The moral of this story? Do not make someone look silly, unless you are ready to look silly, too.

19 The Bat who changed sides

Fedro

Once, all winged creatures were battling against four-footed animals, with victories on both sides. As the bat had wings and feet, he went on each side in turn, whichever he thought was winning. When peace came, the bat was hated for changing sides to suit himself. In the end, he was so ashamed that he hid away in the dark of night. And so it is to this day.

20 The Stings of the Bee

Aesop

"It's not fair!" the bees told Mother Nature. "We buzz around, working hard to make honey! But it is people who eat it!"

"That is true," agreed Mother Nature. "But what do you want me to do about it?"

"We want our stings to do harm," they said firmly, "to kill anyone coming near our beehives at any time!"

Mother Nature said nothing. But in her eyes was a look of dismay at such a cruel request.

"But you have been given stings to defend yourselves," she said at last. "If you wish, you can use them to hurt those who disturb you. But if you do, your sting will remain buried in the human flesh, and you will not be able to get it out. And that will be the end for you. Losing your sting, you will also lose your life!"

The bees learned a bitter lesson. The more you risk, the more you stand to lose.

21 The Eagle and the Snake

from Germany

An eagle was perched high up in an oak tree. "What a great bird I am!" it thought. "I make my nest here, beneath the clouds! I laugh at thunder and rain!" Then he noticed a snake on the same branch. "You-you don't have wings!" it cried. "And you can't have jumped up here! So how did you do it?"

The snake gave a hiss. "I just sneezed! And here I am!"

22 The Wolf and the Woodcutter

Fedro

A wolf was hiding from a hunter. "Don't give me away!" he pleaded to a woodcutter.

"Any sign of a wolf?" called the hunter.

"He went to the left!" said the man, moving his eyes to the right. But the hunter did not understand.

"Do thank your tongue!" the wolf told the man afterwards. "But not your eyes!"

23 The Parrot and the Duck

from Korea

There was once a man who had a lovely talking parrot who could say lots of words. One of his neighbours tried to buy this parrot many times.

"You can offer me any amount," the parrot's owner said each time, "but I shall never sell this bird, not to you or anyone else!"

One day, the neighbour came carrying a duck under his arm.

"Buy this duck!" said the man. "It is such a clever thinker! And what are empty words compared to deep thought?"

"Perhaps you are right.." said the parrot's owner after some thought. "What do you want for the duck?"

"Your parrot!" came the reply. "Plus a bag of gold!"

"Done!"

And so the foolish man lost his talking parrot and a bag of gold. All he had was a duck who went "Quack-Quack!", letting everyone think he was thinking.

24 The Ant and the ear of corn

Leonardo da Vinci

An ant was once returning to his ant-hill with a splendid ear of corn.

Suddenly the seed cried out with a tiny, little voice. "Let me grow! Let me grow, and I shall pay you back a hundred times!"

So the ant let the ear fall. And some time later, on that same spot there grew a beautiful spear of corn, with one hundred golden ears.

25 The Lark who was wise

Aesop

Mother Lark's babies had been born in the cornfield, just as the corn was ripening. She feared the corn would be cut before her chicks could fly. "If anyone comes whilst I am away getting food for us all," she said to the baby birds, "just tell me what they say!"

A little later, the farmer and his son arrived. "The corn is ripe!" said the farmer. "Tomorrow, we must get our friends to help cut it!"

"Farmer's cutting the corn tomorrow!" the chicks told Mother Lark when she came back. "He's getting his friends to help!"

"If he needs help from his friends," she said, "then he won't get the corn cut yet!" Sure enough, the next day there was only the father and his son in the cornfield.

"We must ask our family to help us cut the corn tomorrow!" said the farmer.

"They're getting their family to help cut the corn tomorrow!" the larks told their mother.

"If he needs help from his family," said Mother Lark, "he won't cut the corn tomorrow!"

And so the next day passed. "At dawn tomorrow," said the farmer, "we shall begin cutting the corn ourselves!"

"They plan to cut the corn themselves!" the chicks told Mother Lark. "Tomorrow, at dawn!"

"It is time to move on," she said. "If that is what they said, then that is what they will do." And Mother Lark and her little ones flew to safety.

26 The Goose Feather

Trilussa

A goose and a donkey were both grumbling, because people thought they were stupid.

"When the great poets wrote their masterpieces," cackled the goose, "what did they use?"

"What?" asked the donkey.

"A goose-feather quill!" said the goose.

The donkey thought for a moment. Then it asked, "But where did they get them from?"

27 The Wild Boar and the Lion

from Africa

"You think you're so strong!" said the wild boar to the lion one day. "Well, I am stronger!"

"Oh, no you're not!" roared the lion.

"Yes I am!" grunted the wild boar. "Why, I only have to sneeze to beat you!"

"Prove it!" said the lion. So the wild boar tickled the end of his great nose with a blade of grass, nearly exploding with a huge "ATISHOO!" From one nostril there came a woodland breeze. From the other? The first-ever mouse!

"ATISHOO!" sneezed the lion. From one nostril there came a mighty desert wind. From the other? The first-ever cat!

The cat soon began to chase the mouse, who ran and hid in a hole, quaking with fright.

"See that?" roared the lion. "All you could sneeze was a coward!"

After that, the mouse has always run away from a cat!

28 The Bird-Catcher and the Crested Skylark

Aesop

There is one difference between the crested lark and the ordinary lark.

The ordinary lark has smooth head feathers. The crested lark's head feathers are ruffled up.

When larks were hunted for meat, this tuft often saved the life of the crested lark, because men liked the meat of the ordinary lark. They would often let a crested lark go.

One day, a crested lark saw a man mending his nets. "What are you doing?" it asked.

"I am starting a colony!" said the man shortly.

Believing what the bird-catcher said, the crested lark flew into his net.

Instead, the man caught the bird and held it in his fist.

"If you're starting a colony like this," said the bird, "you won't get any settlers!"

The moral? People who rule by fear and cheating end up alone and despised by everyone.

29 The Eagle and the Harpy

Melegari

A harpy is a legendary monster with a woman's head and body and a bird's claws and wings. Chief of the birds was to be the one who flew best and had the strongest voice. The eagle and harpy were equal in flight. But although the eagle's voice was the loudest, the harpy's cry brought fear to all who heard it. "Only bullies rule by terror!" said Falcon. "The eagle shall be our leader!"

30 The Wise Wolf and the Sheep

Aesop

This is the story of a wolf who was wise as well as hungry. One day, it came across a sheep all on its own. The animal looked so frightened that the wolf approached gently, speaking in a voice as soft as he could make it.

"Do not be afraid, dear sheep, you are free to go where you like! But first, I want to see if you can speak the truth! Just tell me the first three thoughts which come into your mind! What is the first one?"

"Er.. Er.." bleated the sheep, "having met you once, I-I don't want to meet you again!"

"Good! Very good!" sniggered the wolf. "Now let's hear what you have to say next!"

"I-I wish that you would lose the sight of your two eyes!" the sheep blurted out, closing its own eyes and expecting to be killed there and then.

"Good! Very good!" murmured the wolf. "What about the third thing you want to say?"

The sheep opened its eyes and spoke calmly. "I want to see the end of you," it said, "and every other wicked wolf!"

"Oh, yes?" growled the wolf.

"Yes!" said the sheep, now feeling as brave as a lion. "You wolves are always attacking us! Yet we have never done you any harm!"

"That is true," said the wolf at last. "Go then, you are free!"

Truth, you see, is always best and always respected – even among enemies.

Pigs in a Carriage

A FARMER had a pig-sty just outside his farm. This pig-sty had once been a carriage. The seats had been stripped out and the wheels taken off, so that the actual body rested on the ground. In days gone by, it had been a state coach. Now, shreds of silk hanging from the ceiling and carved handles were the only reminders of its former splendour. "Oink-Oink!" grunted the pigs, and the carriage creaked and groaned, because it had got into such a sorry state. "All beauty has gone!" it sighed.

Autumn came, and the pigs were let out to nose around in the forest. Now, blossoms and leaves had fallen from the trees. There were storms, pitiless rain fell without stopping and most of the birds had flown away.

"All beauty has gone!" came the soft voice of the Rose King.

When a rose fades and loses its petals, only the hip remains. Underneath the rose-hip you will find a big moss-type flower of green and red. And that is the Rose King.

"All beauty has gone!" the Rose King said again. "Roses fade and the leaves fall! The birds are silent and the pigs wander around like lords in the forest!"

By then, the nights were cold and the days misty and damp. Even so, a raven sat on a high bough and cawed, "Good! Good!"

The ravens and crows all had large families and they all cawed together, "Good! Good!"

There were more ravens and crows than any other creature in the forest, so they were the majority. And if it is true that the majority is always right, they were saying that there was something good to be found. But, where?

Beneath the tall forest trees, rain had fallen into a dip in the ground, making a big puddle. Here, the pigs splashed about, thinking what a lovely place it was! The older pigs stayed quite still, but the young ones were never still for a moment.

One piglet had a curly ring in its tail. Its mother was so proud, sure that the others were

looking at the curly-ring tail of her little pig!

But the other pigs were thinking about what to eat!

They had heard that the acorns which they liked so much grew at the root of a tree, so they nosed around in the earth.

Then along came a little pig who said that acorns fell down from the branches. Some had fallen on his snout, so he was quite sure that he was right.

"Oink-Oink!" grunted all the older pigs. "There are none of the autumn fruits for us to eat! All beauty has gone!"

But the mother of the little pig with the curly tail said, "No! There is still beauty in the world!"

"Good! Good!" squawked the raven.

"It is finished! Finished!" sighed the Rose King, and it did seem that was true.

It was such a grey and windy day, the rain falling in long, dark streaks. Where were the flowers of the fields? Where were the sweet fruits of the forest? They had all gone!

But – a light shone in the farm-house, showing the farmer and his family and casting its ray among the trees. Here, the grandfather spoke of spring returning, of the forest becoming fresh and green once more, of the roses which would bloom again, and of the beauty which would reign.

The Rose King did not hear the story. He sat huddled in the damp and the rain sighing, "It is finished! Finished!"

And among the pigs who were the lords of the forest, he could hear the grunts of Mother Pig and her piglet with the curly-ring tail.

"Everyone cries that all the beautiful things have gone, and dreams of their return," she thought to herself. "But the beauty of my piglet's tail is always there, ready for me to see all year round! Like me, there is always someone who can look and see something beautiful!"

Hans Andersen

July

1 The Lion, the Jackal and the Fox

from Somalia

The fox and the jackal asked the lion if they could go hunting with him.

The lion agreed, and the hunt began. Soon, they had caught a gazelle.

"Divide it up!" the lion told the jackal.

"The front portion is for Your Majesty," said the jackal, "the rear portion is mine, and Fox gets the rest of – ouch!"

The jackal winced in pain as the lion's fist came down on his head.

But the lion hardly seemed to take any notice. Instead, he turned to the fox. "Now!" said the king of the beasts. "You divide it up!"

"The insides and the feet are for me and the hyena," said the fox all in one breath. "And the rest is for you, Your Majesty!"

"You are most kind!" said the lion. "How did you learn such noble manners for your king?"

"Seeing what you did to the jackal!" answered the fox.

2 The Rattlesnake's Concert

Melegari

The rattlesnake thought he was such a wonderful musician as he rattled the bony rings at the tip of its tail! One day he invited all the other snakes to a concert.

The first piece he played with his tail straight up. *"Crack-ack-crack-ack-crack-ack!"*

Then he bowed. But the audience were silent.

Next, the rattlesnake hung by his teeth from a tree, so that his tail hung down. Then he began again. *"Crack-ack-ack-crack! Crack-ack-ack-crack!"*

He bowed again. But still the audience were silent.

So the rattlesnake wound itself around the tree, and with his tail in a straight line, began rattling. *"Ack-crack-crack! Ack-crack-crack!"*

Still the audience were silent. "Really!" he rattled. "What is it you what?"

"Sssh!" a viper hissed back. "We want to go to sleep!"

3 The Mosquito and the Swallow

from Latvia

As Noah's ark floated across the flooded waters of the earth, one of the animals found that water was leaking in through the hull.

"It's only a little hole!" said the snake. "I can plug it with my body! And as a reward, Noah, when the flood is over, I shall eat the meat with the sweetest blood that there is!"

"Right!" the other animals cried together, before Noah could say anything.

So he gave the mosquito the job of finding out whose meat had the sweetest blood.

Well, the flood went down. But the mosquito was still searching. It was about to go back to Noah, when it met a swallow. And this swallow had found out that, second only to insects, the sweetest blood in the world belonged to humans. Then the swallow gave the mosquito such a big kiss that it returned to the ark with a swollen lip!

From that moment, it could only make a buzzing sound – so nobody was able to understand that, second only to insects, human blood was the sweetest.

"I know!" cried the swallow. "The sweetest-tasting blood is that of the toad!"

The snake had eaten plenty of toads, so he knew this was not true. *"Glop!"* it went, trying to get the bird.

But the swallow flew off, so all the snake could bite was its tail – which to this day, shows the two sharp points at either side of the snake's mouth.

4 The Donkey and the Nightingale

Krylov

A donkey asked a nightingale if he could hear her song.

The nightingale was very pleased. She burst forth with a chorus of beautiful trills, superb notes and lovely melody.

"I shall tell the cockerel about you," said the donkey when she had finished. "Maybe he will give you lessons!"

Many people judge things they know nothing about, too!

5 The Sick Lion and the Fox

Aesop

Lion was pretending to be ill. He sent word to all the animals that he would like visitors, one at a time. Each one was eaten up. But when the fox came, he stayed outside the lion's den. "Come inside, my friend!" roared the lion.

"I shall stay outside, thank you!" said the fox. "I do not like to see so many footprints going in, but none coming out."

6 The Three Cockerels

Manzoni

A man was taking three cockerels to the house of a learned lawyer. The cockerels were to pay for the help which the lawyer had given him. Still alive, those three plump cockerels had been tied together, and the man carried them along by their feet.

Every so often, the man gave the cockerels a violent shake, trying to stop their clucking and their wriggling.

And with each shake, the heads of those cockerels beat against each other.

Not being able to understand what was happening, they got angry, each blaming the other for their discomfort, and pecking at each other wherever they could.

Those poor cockerels! They were all sharing the same misfortune!

Yet they spent all their time arguing and making their suffering worse – instead of trying to help themselves and making things better.

7 The Dog who was Thankful

Trilussa

A man was eating a chicken. And as he ate, he gave some to the dog and then the cat. When there was nothing more on his plate, the cat said, "I can see you have finished! So I am going!"

But the dog did not move. "Good dog!" said the man. "At least you keep me company!"

"Yes," said the dog, "because I know you are sure to eat another chicken before long!"

8 The Cyclist and the Tortoise

Melegari

A racing cyclist was resting at the side of the road – when along came a tortoise! "Poor thing!" said the cyclist. "You have no idea of speed, timing... nobody would bother racing against you!"

"But, the world is round, isn't it?" said the tortoise. "So, whether we race or move slowly, we will finish back where we started!"

9 The Bear and the Little Goats

Asbiomsen and Moe

Three billy goats wanted to eat the grass in a certain field on the other side of a certain stream, across a certain bridge – under which there lived a certain big bear.

"Who is on my bridge?" cried the bear as the first billy goat came trotting along.

"The smallest of the three billy goats!" he cried. "Can I cross the stream and eat the grass in the field?"

"Stay there!" growled the bear. "I am going to eat you!"

"No!" cried the little goat. "The second billy goat is much bigger than me! What a fine meal he will make for you!"

"Very well!" growled the bear. Soon, the second billy goat came trotting along.

"Stay there!" growled the bear. "I am going to eat you!"

"No!" cried the second billy goat. "Wait until my big brother comes along! He will make a lovely feast for you!"

"Very well!" said the bear.

The bridge shook under the weight of the biggest billy goat! "Stay there!" growled the bear. "I am going to eat you!"

"Just try it!" came the reply, and the bear felt two great horns digging in his tummy!

The bear was on the bridge when those goats came back from eating that certain grass in that certain field. All three had grown so fat that the bridge collapsed as they walked across! And the bear? He fell into the river!

10 The Talking Parrot

Hebel

A barber had a parrot which repeated words and phrases it heard in the shop. Sometimes, it would introduce these words into people's conversations, often with comical results!

One day, the barber was trimming the mayor's whiskers. "I heard your speech in the square last Sunday!" he said.

"What did you think of it?" asked the mayor.

"What a bore!" cackled the parrot. Everyone laughed so much that the bird became very vain and flew off to become king of the wild birds. Instead, it finished up in the net of a bird-catcher.

"Shampoo, sir?" said the parrot – and the man knew he belonged to the barber.

"If you do not know how to climb, you are sure to fall!" said the barber when he collected the bird. "What more did you want from me?"

"A tip!" cackled the parrot.

11 The Marten and the Squirrel

Melegari

Nobody could beat the squirrel at climbing trees! But another good climber was the marten – also an eater of squirrels! Usually the marten hunts by night and sleeps during the day. But one time, he came out of his lair earlier than usual, and saw the squirrel taking some nuts to his drey at the top of a high oak tree.

Seeing the marten, Squirrel began climbing the tree. But the marten was after him in a flash. Soon he was only inches away from the squirrel's tail.

"I am beaten now!" thought the squirrel. Then he thought again. "Or, perhaps not..."

And he carried on, climbing and jumping from branch to branch – going round and round the tree trunk as he went!

The marten tried following the squirrel. But everything started going round and round! Feeling dizzy, it fell to the ground – with a shower of nuts falling on its head for good measure!

12 The Two Mules and the Bandits

de la Fontaine

"I belong to some bandits," one mule told another on the road. "That's why I am carrying gold pieces!"

"Lucky you!" said the second. "I am only carrying peas!" But the second mule was glad shortly after, when the bandits beat their mule for giving away the secret of the pieces of gold – and he was left to continue his journey in peace.

13 The Song of the Cuckoo

from Madagasca

Everyone has heard stories about the lazy cuckoo, who waits until another bird flies away and lays her eggs in its nest. The cuckoo's eggs hatch before the others, with the chicks coming out and thinking themselves the masters!

But this is a story which sees things in another way.

The Great Spirit of Africa once asked all the creatures on earth to sing in chorus with him.

The chorus went on and on – until the animals' throats got dry and they had to stop. Only the cuckoo went on singing and singing. "Bravo!" cried the Great Spirit. "You deserve a reward! Because you are not tired by singing with me and for me, from now on, when you want to lay eggs, you need not build a nest! Lay your eggs in the nests of other birds, among the others. Then they will hatch them for you, leaving you free to sing *"Cuckoo! Cuckoo!"*"

14 The Sick Hen and the Marten

Aesop

A hen was not laying well. From behind the netting of her coop she saw a marten enter. "I am the doctor," he said. "I have come to see you!"

"Go to the back of the yard," said the hen, "and turn left!"

The marten did this – and found himself looking at a spider's web. "I feel so much better!" he heard the hen saying. "Because the doctor has gone!"

15 The Duck and the Falcon

Leonardo da Vinci

A falcon was flying around the banks of a mountain lake, when he caught sight of a duckling a little way from Mother Duck and the other ducklings.

"I could eat that silly little duck in one mouthful!" cawed the falcon, diving down.

"Look out!" cried Mother Duck, who had just seen the danger. The duckling dived under the water, chased by the falcon, the tips of its wings brushing the ripples. For a few moments, it too went under the water, frightening the little fish and freshwater shrimps.

By now, the duckling was safely back with its family. But the falcon, coming to the surface, was exhausted, cold and wet through.

The mighty bird of prey struggled towards the bank, flapping its wings feebly, thinking how easy it was to do stupid things when you were hungry – and that strength is not enough to stay afloat.

16 The Mule and the Coyote

from North America

A Red Indian had trained a mule so well that he could send it here and there, fetching and carrying loads by itself.

One day, as the mule plodded along loaded with goats' cheeses, a coyote came trotting beside him. "What a lovely smell of goats' cheese!" said the coyote. "Can I have some?"

"No!" said the little mule. "My master will scold me!"

"You're so good!" sighed the coyote. "If I had a son like you, I would jump for joy! And – *hop! hop! hop!* – the coyote made three jumps – and ran off with a cheese in his mouth!

"One cheese is missing!" said his master when the mule returned. "How is that?"

"It was that coyote!" exclaimed the little mule. "Let me find him, and I shall make him pay!"

Off he went. And from that day to this, whenever a mule senses a stealthy step nearby, it kicks out like a bullet from a rifle!

17 The Wolf and the Guard Dog

Fedro

A hungry wolf met a dog. "How do you look so well?" he asked.

"I just eat and drink and keep guard," said the dog. "You could do the same!"

"Perhaps," said the wolf. "What's that round your neck?"

"My collar," said the dog. "A lead hooks on it, so that I can be tied up each day, and –"

"I'm off!" said the wolf. "I prefer to be hungry and free to being fed and on a lead!"

18 The Fox with a Tail of Straw

Gradi

There was once a handsome fox, who, alas, had lost its long, thick tail in a trap. So he decided to make himself a false one.

He wove some straw, which he trimmed and tinted with bilberry juice. Then he stuck it on so well that the straw tail looked quite real!

But, like anything else made of straw, there was the danger of the new tail catching fire.

The cockerel, who had long ears as well as a long neck, heard about the straw tail.

He told the farmer that at the close of the evening, lots of little fires should be lit all around the farmyard. And as the fox looked on, the fires crackled, as if to say, "if you come near, you will go up like a firework!"

So the fox with the straw tail had to hunt away from the farmyard, chasing mice and frogs – which, to a hungry fox, just cannot compare with a plump, tender chicken!

19 The Raven and the Unicorn

Meissner

Legend says the unicorn was a white horse with a spiral horn at the front of its head – and a bad temper! One day it boasted to a raven that with just one butt from his horn, he could knock down a mountain! Then he lowered his head, ran forward, and – the mountain broke its horn and he fell to the ground like an empty sack. "Pride always comes before a fall!" croaked the raven.

20 The Fox and the Grapes

Aesop

A fox was looking for food, when he saw some magnificent vines with bunches of lovely purple grapes, just asking to be eaten! The fox jumped up, trying to get one.. or a half.. or a mouthful.. But he could not reach them. "I bet they're sour, anyway!" he snarled – as angry as those who, when they cannot do something, blame the circumstances.

21 The Oyster and the Crab

Melegari

A crab once wanted to taste an oyster – which, as you may know, many people like to eat!

An oyster feeds on tiny creatures which live in the sea. When it needs food, it opens the two halves of its shell. But as soon as it senses danger, the oyster closes its shell, staying safely inside. Of course, the crab wanted to eat the oyster without fear of being trapped between the two halves of its shell!

Now the oyster, not being able to move about, liked to hear news. So when the crab found a whelk hiding among the seaweed, he asked the whelk to tell some news to the oyster.

The oyster was very pleased to see the whelk stop by his shell, wriggling about as if to say, "I've got something to tell you!"

It opened its shell, and the whelk moved nearer, wedging itself between the two halves of the oyster's shell.

"There's a rumour," said the whelk, "that the turtle has had a fight with the octopus and left him without any whiskers!"

"Really?" breathed the oyster, enjoying the gossip so much, it did not notice that the crab was crawling up behind.

Only as the crab jumped forward did the oyster try to close its shell – but the whelk's shell kept it open just wide enough for the crab to get its pincers inside..

Pity nobody had told the oyster – there is no harm being curious – as long as you are careful at the same time.

22 Mother and Father Pig

from Ireland

Every so often, Father Pig would say to his son, "Let us go out into the world!"

Together they would leave the pig-sty, go out and explore – until the farmer sent a dog to chase them safely back into the pig-sty.

Then Mother Pig would say to her son, "Promise that you will never do that again!"

But, of course, he always did. Father Pig saw to that!

23 The Porcupine and the Jackal

from Africa

The porcupine is a very slow, peace-loving animal – quite different to the jackal which runs here and there, gobbling food left by other animals.

One day, the jackal said to the porcupine, "I hear there's some lovely meat on the top of that hill! Let's have a race, and see who can get it!"

"But you know you're much faster than me!" said the porcupine. "The meat should go to the elder of us two!"

"Well," said the jackal, "I was born forty thousand centuries before the world began!"

The porcupine began to cry. "You've just reminded me," he sobbed. "I've forgotten to collect my old-age pension!"

The jackal fell back on its tail, speechless.

And before he could get his breath back, the porcupine was halfway up the hill, already looking forward to some meat for supper!

24 The Mouse who wanted a Wife

Maria de Francia

A mouse wanted to marry the daughter of the sun! The sun hid her behind a cloud, and the cloud sent for the wind to blow her further away. Only a tower tried standing against the wind. But that fell down – because the mouse had gnawed its foundations away.

So because he destroyed one thing, that mouse lost something more dear to him.

25 The Baby Jackal who wanted to play

Folgore

"Let me play!" cried a baby jackal, rolling over on the grass with a little elephant and hippopotamus. Before long, he was underneath both of them!

He got home with bruises all over his back. And as Mother Jackal helped make him feel better, she thought, "Why are the little ones often squashed by the big ones – yet the big ones never squash each other?"

26 The Cuckoo, the Nightingale and the Donkey

Fortiguerri

The cuckoo and the nightingale were great rivals. The cuckoo prided himself on his clear notes, the nightingale on her beautiful trills. And each time the two birds met, they finished up arguing.

So they agreed on a contest, with the donkey as the judge. His long ears, they thought, would not miss a single note!

"Right!" said the donkey, when they asked him. "Each of you must sing something in turn!"

The cuckoo began, singing a dozen or so times *"Cuckoo! Cuckoo!"* one after the other.

Then the nightingale filled the wood with a lovely cascade of notes, going on until the donkey brayed for her to stop.

"The nightingale sings well!" said the donkey. "But the cuckoo sings better, because he has more style!"

How many of us waste time seeking the approval of those whose opinions are worthless?

27 The Goat and the Goatherd

Aesop

A goatherd's son was bringing goats back from pasture. One was still grazing, so he threw a stone to make her move. Instead, it broke one of her horns.

"Don't tell Father!" he begged. "I did not mean to hit you!"

"You think he will not notice?" said the goat. "How can I hide what is plain for all to see?"

Try to cover up misdeeds – and you are soon found out!

28 The Cat, the Mouse and the Sausage

Krylov

A shopkeeper hated mice. So, he got a cat to chase away any mouse who dared to come near!

All went well, until one day, as the cat slept, a tiny mouse managed to get in and made little bites in a huge sausage hanging from the ceiling!

By the time the man noticed, the mouse – thanks to all that sausage – had become big enough to eat the cat!

The news soon reached the newspapers, the television and the radio!

"A supermarket protected by a cat?" said the headlines. "Has the shopkeeper never heard of modern electronic apparatus and infra-red rays with loud cat noises and alarms linked directly to a police station?"

The shopkeeper read all the reports. So – he bought another cat and kept it in the shop with an alarm on its collar!

This is what's known as making the best of both worlds!

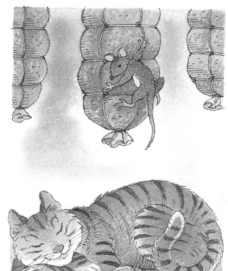

29 The Shepherd Wolf

Aesop

One day a wolf came across a flock of sheep grazing. The sheep-dog was asleep, along with the shepherd, who had taken off his cloak, hat and sandals. Now, he snored loudly, his crook beside him.

The wolf crept up and took the man's cloak. He put it on, then picked up the crook and clapped the hat on his head, pretending to be the shepherd!

The wolf made a signal with the crook as he had seen the shepherd do, and the flock began taking a few steps towards him. But this was all much too slow for the wolf! So he made the signal again, and the sheep took another step.

"Are you going to hurry up?" he burst out impatiently. Hearing his gruff cries, the sheep stopped, then began running away, one after the other, waking the shepherd and the dog. And that was the end of the wolf! In the end, impostors and cheats are always found out.

30 The Mole and the Rabbits

Florian

Will you admit that you cannot do something? Or are you like the mole in this story? Moles cannot see well. So the rabbits did not know why he wanted a blindfold to play Blind Man's Buff! "Is that all right?" they asked, tying it over his eyes.

"Pull it a bit tighter!" said the mole. "I can still see!"

He took a step, and fell – *bump!* on the ground!

31 The Wolf and the Oxen

Melegari

At the time when tractors had not been invented, two oxen were pulling a plough.

They were doing the job so unwillingly and so badly that the furrows were wavy and zig-zag – none of them straight.

"Can't we do something which is not so boring?" one of the animals asked the ploughman.

"No!" the man shouted. "Now, work straight, or you'll get eaten by the wolf!"

"And I'M just ready for a meal!" roared the wolf, showing his teeth.

"No" cried the ploughman. "I only said.."

"I know what you said!" snarled the wolf. "And those oxen are NOT pulling the plough straight! So I shall eat them!"

"But that's not fair!" the ploughman burst out.

"I shall decide what is fair!" roared the wolf.

"Maauu –!" lowed one of the oxen. "No! WE shall decide what is fair and just!"

And before the ploughman knew what was happening, the two oxen lurched forward, wrenching the plough from his hands. Together, they lowered their heads and butted the wolf in the stomach with their strong horns! Next minute, the wolf was knocked to the ground, bumps and bruises all over his body.

Then the oxen went quietly back to work, pulling the plough in straight furrows.

No matter what the job is, a change always does us good!

The Hare and the Tar Baby

THERE had been no rain for a long, long time. So the forest animals – Bear, Elephant, Wolf, Monkey, Fox, Lion and the rest – ending with Hare – went to seek an underground spring.

Everyone began searching – everyone, that is, except Hare.

"Don't expect me to dig underground!" he protested. "I am not a mole!"

"Right!" said the others. "We shan't let you have even a drop of the water we find!"

But Hare only laughed.

Well, the animals dug and dug – until, at last, they found water! They all had a lovely drink and a bath, then returned to their homes.

Next day when they returned to the well, Hare's footprints were all around the hole! He had stolen their water during the night!

The only way to stop him doing it again was to take it in turns to guard the well.

"I shall be first!" said the bear. So at sunset, the other animals went to bed, leaving him on guard.

He did not hear Hare crawling out from under a bush. But Hare saw the bear on guard, and he began to sing.

"La-la-la-la! Te-tum-te-tum!"

Bear looked all around. And because the song made him want to dance – he danced and he pirouetted! He turned and spun and waltzed, moving far enough from the well for Hare, still singing, to have a nice drink and a bath before leaving!

Next morning, the animals saw Hare's footprints. "Huh!" they grumbled. "So much for Bear guarding the well!"

"I was awake!" Bear protested. "The only time I left the well was to see where this lovely music was coming from!"

The other animals talked things over. "Monkey," they said at last, "it is up to you to keep guard tonight!"

Evening came, out came the stars – and when he saw Monkey, the hare began singing again. "La-la-la-la! Te-tum-te-tum!"

"Where's that music coming from?" the monkey wondered. "It makes me want to dance!"

And – Monkey began to dance and dance, skipping and jumping, hopping and leaping and finishing up a long way from the well! Down went the hare, took all the water he wanted before returning to his hiding place in the wood!

"You're a silly sausage!" the other animals told Monkey next day. "Just like Bear!"

"But I didn't mean to leave the well!" said Monkey. "Only I heard this music, and –"

"Wait!" interrupted Fox." What we need to guard the well is a tar baby, as sticky as can be! See what Hare makes of that!"

And for the rest of the day, they collected the stickiest resin which they could find from the trees and made a ball of tar. They moulded it in the shape of a little man, dressed it in straw and old clothes, and put him beside the well!

As night fell, the hare came out of the wood and saw the tar baby! As he had done before, he began to sing. "La- la-la-la! Te-tum-te-tum!"

But, of course, the tar baby did not move. So the hare moved closer and sang again. "La-la-la-la! Te-tum-te-tum!" Then he stopped. The tar baby still had not moved.

Hare went closer. "Move off!" he shouted at the tar baby. "Let me get at that well!"

The angry hare punched the tar baby so hard that his paw stuck in the tar!

"Let me go!" he shouted. "Do you want another punch?" And because his left paw was sticky with tar, he punched out with his right. That stuck in the tar as well!

"Let me go!" Hare shrieked again. "Do you want a kick?"

Soon, the right foot was stuck in the tar, quickly followed by the left foot!

"Let me GO!" screamed Hare, now in a complete rage. "I can still give you a head butt!"

And – *splat!* – Hare's nose was stuck in the tar!

And that is how the animals found him next morning. They left him for a while, stuck to the tar baby, then they pulled him off by his ears – which is why a hare's ears are still long to this day!

Stories from Uncle Remus

1 The Gypsy and the Dragon

Afanasjev

A gypsy was passing through a town where the only person was a man, crying, "Tomorrow the dragon returns! He has already eaten everyone else. Soon it will be my turn!"

"I shall give that dragon what it deserves!" said the gypsy, settling down for the night.

Early next day, the dragon appeared.

"I can prove I am stronger than you!" cried the gypsy.

"Really?" roared the dragon, and began hissing like a steam engine.

"My turn!" said the gypsy. "But bandage your eyes first. Otherwise my steam will scald your eyes!"

The dragon sniggered as the gypsy tied a handkerchief around its eyes. Then the man whistled like a locomotive, and gave the dragon such a blow that the beast was no more.

So you see – the wicked are always defeated in the end.

2 The Little Spider and the Grapes

Leonardo da Vinci

Among some bunches of grapes hung a web, once the home of a naughty, little spider – little, because his web was only tiny. And, naughty? Well, that was what the flies said, once a few had been caught in the spider's web!

But the spider was turned out of its home once the grapes began getting picked.

Then they were washed, put into a vat and pressed, ready to be made into wine.

And that is how the spider found itself floating in the pulp and grape juice.

A little fly saw the spider and cried, "Hey! How are things in the red sea?"

"About the same as they are for a fly in a spider's web!" the spider called back.

"So, we are equal!" said the fly.

"Yes!" cried the spider. "As bad as each other!" And it began swimming in the juice, then the wine – the two products we get from grapes.

3 The Two Cockerels, the Eagle and the Hen

Aesop

Two cockerels fought over a hen. The one which was beaten went to rest. The other flew to a roof-top. "Cock-a-doodle-doo!" he crowed. "I am the winner!"

Hearing him, an eagle dived down and seized the cockerel in his great claws. The other cockerel married the hen and lived happily ever after.

It is never good to boast after victory.

4 The Laugh of the Rattlesnake

Melegari

A rattlesnake was going along when he saw a pair of serpent-eater birds out hunting. So the rattlesnake hid in a bush and held his breath.

When they were two or three paces away from the bush, the rattlesnake gave his tail a sharp *"Crack-ack!"*

"Don't tread on a dry twig!" said the serpent-eater to his wife. "All the snakes will know we are here!"

"Crack-ack!" went the rattlesnake's tail.

"You did it again!" said the serpent-eater and a fierce argument began.

When they had gone, the rattlesnake began to laugh, making his tail rattle loudly.

"Crack-ack! Crack-ack-ack! Crack-ack-ack!"

Luckily the birds were already a long way off. The rattlesnake did not think that they would see the funny side of the joke he had played on them!

5 The Eyes of the Snail

Belloc

Imagine a cow having eyes on her horns like a snail! She would be able to see everything from her stall! She might even perform to great applause!

But all this could make her conceited – unlike the snail, who goes back in its shell at the least sound.

People who can accept criticism with patience are like that snail.

6 The Crafty Fox and the Porcupine

Firenzuola

Porcupine and Fox were coming back from battle. "Why wear that armour of spines?" asked Fox. "The fighting is over!"

"True!" said Porcupine. That night, before going to bed, he took off his armour. And as he slept, Fox ate him without fear of hurting his tongue!

Beware of advice from those who have their own interests at heart!

7 The Turkish Wolf and the Dervish

from Turkey

Just as there are monks in Christian religions, the Muslim faith have dervishes, men who go around helping poor people and preaching sermons.

Well, there was this wolf who went around Turkey stealing sheep from their flocks. One day, he met a dervish, and the man soon began lecturing him.

"I know you're up to some evil plan!" he told the wolf.

"You are going in search of some poor innocent creature to eat! When will you stop being so greedy?"

And so the good dervish went on. But the wolf was not listening. His mind was on his empty stomach!

"Good dervish!" he said at last, "would you shorten your lecture? I can smell a sheep behind that little hill, so I really must go!"

And off he went.

Have you ever noticed that? The more greedy people are, the less they want to listen.

8 The Squirrel's jump

Melegari

A marten always hoped Squirrel would fall into his mouth! "You jump well!" he said. "But Monkey can do a somersault!"

"Like this?" said Squirrel. He did not know height was needed for somersaults in the air! He jumped as usual, and fell – much to the marten's delight.

So do not be like Squirrel. Be sure you know all the facts before trying something new.

9 The Firefly and the Eaglet

Melegari

"Hey, little worm with wings!" cried an eaglet to a firefly. "What are you doing in these parts?"

"I fly higher than any bird!" said the firefly. "If ever you meet the eagle's son, tell him that I have already beaten the others, and now I am coming below to beat the eagles!"

"I can only advise you not to try it!" said the eaglet. "The sun is setting, so I cannot go with you!"

"All right!" said the firefly. flying higher. "You can go down, and I shall see you later!"

And the eaglet managed to fly to the nest, thinking how mad the firefly was!

But the firefly flew up and up until he reached the nearest star and sat gasping for breath.

Then he grabbed a little piece and shone it towards the earth, making up his mind that he would never, ever let it go. That bright light was his proof of victory!

10 The Fallen Sparrow

Turgeniev

A dog and a hunter were going home when they noticed a baby sparrow which had fallen from the nest.

The dog went closer, baring its teeth as Mother Bird flew down in front of her chick. That great mouth struck fear in the heart of the little sparrow. But still she began to squawk and jump up at the dog, risking her own life for the sake of her chick.

The hunter stepped forward to stop the dog frightening the bird. But the dog, seeing such courage, began slowly backing away, put to shame by the bravery of that little Mother Sparrow.

How glad the dog was to hear the hunter calling him. And together they went on their way, the hunter's game-bag full of the still-warm bodies of animals and birds he had caught.

And with each step they took, so the bag seemed to get heavier and heavier.

11 The Fisherman and the Dancing Fish

Aesop

A fisherman played his flute, dreaming of fish dancing on the waves and falling at his feet. But when he opened his eyes, there were none there. So he put down his flute and cast his net. When he drew it in, it was full of fish, twitching as if they were dancing. "So!" he said. "You dance, now that I do not play?"

Like him, there are those who do things at the wrong time!

12 The Wolf and the Lamb

Aesop

A wolf and a lamb were drinking from a mountain stream. "Lamb!" said the wolf. "You're making the water muddy!"

But, as Wolf was up higher than the lamb, this could not be true. So the lamb answered back. "No I'm not!"

"Enough!" snarled the wolf. "You were rude to my father last year!"

"Your father?" the lamb bleated again. "Last year? I was not even born then!"

"Well, you have grown!" said the wolf. "No wonder, eating all the grass in my fields!"

"But I don't have any teeth!" protested the lamb. "I still take milk from my mother!"

"One excuse after another!" snarled the wolf. "And I am still going to eat you!"

This story shows someone who is determined to do harm will not listen to reason.

13 The Woodpecker and the Pillar

Baldi

A woodpecker who wanted to build a new nest thought he would try something different to the usual tree-trunk. So he decided on a marble pillar!

Toc! Toc! Toc! he pecked hard. But all he got was a pain in his beak!

"No, thank you!" he told the pillar at last – as well as he could, through his dented beak. "A nest of marble would be too cold!"

14 The Dog, the Cat, the Frog and the Ring

from China

A husband and wife had a ring which was said to bring good luck to whoever owned it. Perhaps they thought that a ring could not have such power.

Anyway, they sold it.

But as soon as the ring went out of the house, bad luck came in. There was nothing but want and hunger, not only for the husband and wife, but also the dog and the cat who lived with them.

The animals knew that the ring was kept in a casket in a big house. So they decided to get it back.

"You catch a mouse," the dog told the cat, "and promise to spare its life if it chews at the lock on the casket and brings out the ring!"

So the cat caught the mouse, and carried it in its mouth along the street, then across a river, and in through a door which led to the casket.

When the cat and the dog got the ring (which the cat kept hidden in its mouth), they set the mouse free. Then they crossed back over the river. The cat took a short cut and arrived home much quicker than the dog. And when she gave the ring back to the husband and the wife, they were so grateful. But they scolded the dog when he arrived, thinking he had wasted time, going for a walk.

The cat liked being praised. So it did not bother to explain or come to the defence of the dog. Then, how the dog hated the cat! And from that day onwards, cats and dogs have been enemies!

15 The Little Dog and the Elephant

Krylov

A man came riding down a street on an elephant. The circus had come to town! Suddenly, a little dog went right up to the elephant's trunk and began to bark.

"Stop that!" trumpeted the elephant. "I could make mincemeat of you!"

"That's why I am barking!" cried the puppy. "So that people will say what a brave dog I am!"

16 The Dream of the Singing Cockerel

Chaucer

Mother Fox had never been able to trick the singing cockerel. As well as being handsome, he was also clever. No wonder many hens were in love with him!

But the singing cockerel loved only the little red hen, singing his first song for her, each morning – until one day, she found him trembling with fright!

"I dreamed of a monster!" he told the little red hen.

"Don't tell me that scared you!" she snapped. "I thought you were so brave!"

"But it was a horrible dream!" the cockerel protested.

"Maybe you are ill," said the hen. "Let me make some medicine to help you get better!" The singing cockerel did not really like taking medicine. But, to please the little red hen, he swallowed it down without a murmur.

That night he dreamed of marrying Mother Fox!

But he did not say a word to the little red hen!

17 The Canary and the Poet

Melegari

A poet spent almost all her time writing or reading.

She only broke off to feed her canary, which she kept in a cage.

And although she often forgot to close the door, the canary never wanted to escape.

Until one day, as the poet was giving the bird some fresh drinking water, she said, "You know, some day, I shall have to put you down on paper!"

It was an innocent remark. What she meant was, "One day, I shall write a poem about you!"

But the canary thought the poet meant, "I shall see that you die on some paper!"

The words made him tremble with fear. He awaited his chance. And when she opened the cage to give him some lettuce and forgot to close the door, the canary pecked it open and flew out of the window.

It is so important to make sure that those around us understand what we say.

18 The Elephant – King of the Jackals!

Tolstoy

One day, a jackal said to the elephant, "We once had a king, but no more. Now, my fellow jackals have instructed me to offer you the throne! If you accept, we shall carry out all your orders!"

"I accept!" said the elephant, very pleased.

But, that was before he had to plod across the muddy marshes to where the crowning ceremony was to take place! Poor elephant! Before he knew what was happening, he had fallen over in the mud!

"Pull me out!" he shouted.

"Hold on to my tail with your royal trunk!" cried the leader of the jackals. "I shall pull you out at once!"

"What, this little tail, all thin and stringy?" thundered the elephant. "Impossible!"

"If something is impossible," sniggered the jackal, "then you cannot order me to do it! Silly old elephant! I do not think the throne of the jackals is for you!"

19 The Bees and the Hornets

de la Fontaine

The hornets and the bees were arguing about a hive and the honey inside. The hornets said it was theirs, but the bees said it belonged to them.

The case finished up being judged by an old wasp. There were questions, inspections and investigations. But nothing was decided. "Let us all go to the wood," the bees' lawyer suggested at last. "Then you can put both hornets and bees to work. We shall make a new hive, and the hornets, too. Then once we compare the new hive with the old one, we shall see who the old hive belongs to!"

The hornets said that was a stupid idea, and waited to hear what the judge had to say.

"The suggestion of the bees makes good sense," said the wasp, "far more than papers and arguments! So I say that the old nest belongs to the bees, and it is no good the hornets buzzing about it any longer!"

20 The Fox and the Leopard

Aesop

A leopard is a big, powerful animal with its thick, spotted fur and graceful body. One day, a leopard was boasting to Fox about how beautiful he was. As for Fox – he gave that leopard the answer he deserved! "You are beautiful, certainly!" he nodded. "But beauty is only on the outside. Far better to have a mind which is quick, alert and ready to learn!"

21 Strength in Numbers

Melegari

The rattlesnake was very proud of the sound he could make with his tail.

"If men can charm snakes with music, why shouldn't I do the same with our enemies?" he demanded. "Send word to the sparrowhawk! Tell him that I challenge him to a duel!"

"Very well!" squawked the sparrowhawk when he received the message. And later that same day, he found himself face to face with the rattlesnake.

"Look me in the eye!" cried the rattlesnake. And he made a splendid rattle with his tail. *"Crack-ack-ack!"*

The sparrowhawk just sat there, beak wide open, seeming bewitched by the rhythm.

"We've won!" cried the snakes in a chorus. Together, they attacked the sparrowhawk, so that he never ate snakes again! This story shows that there is strength in numbers. But perhaps music helps a little?

22 The Peacock and the Nightingale

Lessing

A nightingale tried to make friends with other birds in the wood. But they all made some excuse or another – because the nightingale was a better singer than they were. "Jealousy is a horrible thing!" she thought. "Surely I can find one friend!"

And she found – the peacock, who was as beautiful to look at as she was to hear. He had not found any friends, either.

23 Two Owls and a Little Sparrow

Gay

Two old owls were talking together about times which were past.

"Where is the respect and consideration which the Ancient Greeks had for us?" grumbled one. "Why, the city of Athens looked upon the owl as a sacred creature!"

"True!" agreed the second owl. "And one of us was placed upon the helmet of Minerva, goddess of wisdom! But, today? The sparrow who chatters a bit louder than the rest is seen as being better than us!"

"Oh, NO!" chirped a sparrow, who had heard what they said. "Times change, that's all! Owls sacred to Athens and on the helmet of the goddess Minerva belong in legends! Today, everyone knows an owl catches mice far better than any cat! So what is wrong with that?"

"The sparrow is right!" said one of the owls after a pause. "Vanity helps nobody, and achieves nothing!"

24 The Land of Honey

Pestalozzi

An old bear had promised some bear cubs that he would take them to the Land of Honey one day. But that day never arrived. "When will you take us to the Land of Honey?" they kept asking him – until, in the end, he had to think of something. "See that fir tree?" he said, pointing. "I shall climb to the top, just to check the way!" So up went the old bear, just like many other bears had done before him. It was an easy climb!

But at the top, the tree began bending under his weight. And a wind was blowing.

"I cannot take you to the Land of Honey today!" he shouted to the bear-cubs on the ground. "But I–"

There was a loud crack. The tree trunk broke in half – and down he came!

He never did take the bear-cubs to the Land of Honey. But whenever they talk about it, everyone ends up laughing – all except the old bear!

25 The Hunter's Rest

Panciatantra

Long, long ago, a hunter laid down to rest under a tree, bow and arrows by his side. In the tree, both a raven and a flamingo were nesting. The flamingo, seeing the sun moving around the sky and the shade going away from the hunter's face, spread its huge wings to protect the man from the sun's rays.

The bird stayed like this until the hunter, opening his eyes and refreshed by his nap, let out a great yawn.

The raven, always spiteful by nature, threw a shower of twigs and small branches into the hunter's mouth, then flew off to safety.

The hunter looked up to see who had done this to him. Of course, he saw only the flamingo, and thought he was the guilty one. He put an arrow in his bow.

The rest can be imagined. . . as you think on how unwise it is to make friends with those who are spiteful by nature.

26 The Vixen and the Farmer

Krylov

There were once a pair of foxes so expert in stealing chickens, that the farmers were in despair. Then one farmer decided to go and see Mother Fox, the vixen.

"Why eat so many chickens when there is other food about?" he asked. "Stealing from us farmers, too! What a thing to do!"

"I steal," answered the vixen, "because foxes are thieves by nature."

"But why not live an honest life?" the man protested. "Keeping guard over my chickens, for example? I shall give you as many as you need!" The vixen agreed. But soon she was quarrelling with Mr. Fox, then the pheasant, the weasel, the marten and in the end – with herself.

As she told the farmer, many animals are thieves by nature. For them, food without adventure has no taste.

That vixen was soon stealing chickens again.

27 The Two Pockets of Man and Animals

de la Fontaine

"How are you?" Mother Nature asked the monkey one day.

"Very well!" said the monkey. "I have four feet which I can use as well as four hands, so I'm fine! But Bear is stupid and clumsy and no artist would paint his portrait!"

"I heard that!" growled the bear. "If I am clumsy, what about the elephant and his fat legs?"

"I go along slowly and with care!" put in the elephant. And he began to talk about the whale. "All hump and tummy!"

"Well," said Mother Nature, "at least you are all happy with the way you are!"

But she could not help thinking, "Animals are like human beings! And they are all like a poacher, with one pocket at the back of his coat and one at the front! The pocket at the front is full of the faults of others. But the one at the back is for their own faults, the ones they prefer not to see!"

28 The Nest of the Great Tit

Melegari

The great tit is in fact a small bird who rarely nests on branches of trees. And it's all because of the fig tree!

Long ago, the great tit asked the fig tree, "Can I build a nest on one of your branches?"

"As long as the nest is not too heavy!" said the fig tree.

"Wonderful!" cried the great tit, unaware that nobody could climb the fig tree because its wood was so fine. Nor did she know the difference between light and heavy. She used lots of mud, twigs and dry leaves around a thick bed made from tufts of wool, bits of rabbit fur and yarn. It was so heavy that the branch soon went *c-cr-crack – –* and down it came!

The fig tree was angry, the great tit as well – and after that, she never built her nest in another tree. An exaggeration? Perhaps. But the fig tree could also say a few words on the subject – don't you think?

29 The Man and the Eagle

Aesop

One day, a man came across an eagle caught in the net of a bird-catcher and set it free.

A few days later, the same man was sitting down in the shade of a wall when the eagle caught him by surprise and flew off with his hat. The man ran after him, and after a little while, the eagle dropped the hat – just as the wall collapsed. That eagle had saved the man's life.

30 The Oyster and the Mouse

Leonardo da Vinci

Living in a fisherman's house, a mouse had often heard people say how good an oyster tasted! One day, the cat and the man's wife had gone out. This, thought the mouse, was his chance to try an oyster for himself! So he went towards the basket where he knew they were kept.

"Hey!" one of them called. "Take me to the sea and I will give you a nice present!"

"All right!" said the mouse. "But – where are you?"

"In the shell!" came the reply. "You can carry it in your mouth!"

"It's too thick!" protested the mouse. "Open up, then I can carry you!"

That oyster was so keen to get back to the sea, he opened up the two halves of his shell. At once, the mouse put his head right inside, the two halves slammed shut – and he ended up as a treat for the cat!

It was his own fault for betraying a trust.

31 The Basilisk and the Magpie

Melegari

Legend said that a reptile called a basilisk could kill anyone just by looking at them. So, to protect themselves, the other creatures decided to destroy it. They called on the magpie – which, as you know, steals shiny things to take to its nest. Among those shiny things, the bird had a mirror. He held it up for the basilisk to see – and the beast was killed by its own image.

September

The Monkey and the Peasant Man

A PEASANT man was going through a forest with a donkey loaded with wood which he was going to sell. Suddenly, he heard desperate cries for help – cries which were coming from a deep hole.

"Who is there?" called the man going up to the hole.

"Me!" said a voice. "And I am a rich merchant! Save me and you can have half my worldly goods, I promise!"

The peasant unloaded the donkey and took the rope which had tied the wood to its back. One end he tied to a tree, the other end he dropped down into the hole. Next moment, the rope tightened – and up came a monkey, who vanished through the trees at once!

Evidently, it had also been in the hole and caught hold of the rope first! So the man threw down the rope once more.

He pulled and pulled – and this time at the end of the rope was a snake, which soon slithered away between the grass and the stones!

Once more, a voice cried out. "Help me! Help me!"

"Who's that?" the man shouted.

"I'm the merchant who called you the first time! Get me out of this hole, and you can have half my worldly goods!"

"Right!" answered the peasant. "Third time lucky!" And he let down the rope again. This time, the merchant caught it. The man pulled hard – but the merchant was too heavy. So the man tied the rope to the donkey, and between them, they managed to pull the merchant out.

Without a word of thanks, the merchant began making his way towards the city, leaving the peasant with his mouth wide open in amazement.

"Hey!" cried the peasant, catching up with the merchant. "You promised me half your worldly goods! When can I come and collect my reward?"

"You think a nobleman like me has to keep a promise made to a peasant like you?" sneered the merchant. "If you value your life, speak no more about this business!"

Sad and disheartened, the

peasant returned home. And after a restless night, next day he went with his donkey into the forest to collect wood, as usual.

When he came to the place where he had rescued the merchant, he had a surprise. The monkey he had also rescued the day before was there, waiting. Nearby was a great pile of wood, all ready cut and neatly tied and ready to be loaded on the donkey's back!

The same thing happened the day after, and for many more days after that. In a few weeks, the man had earned more money than he had ever earned in months of hard work! It was clear the monkey wanted to repay the peasant for having saved his life.

Then one day as the peasant was going through the forest, he saw the snake at his feet. The snake lifted its head, then made a sign to tell the man to take a shining object from its mouth.

It was a diamond, the biggest which the man had ever seen! He hurried back home and showed it to his wife.

"This is too precious for peasants like us," she said. "Sell it in the town!"

So the man went into town and sold the diamond for a good sum of money. He put it in his money-bag and went home, ready to show his wife.

But when he opened the money-bag – there was another diamond, the same as the first!

"It is not possible!" he cried. "This is the stone which I have already sold!"

Next day, he went back to town, and sold the second diamond. He put the coins in his money-bag, went home – and inside was another diamond!

Before long, the peasant was rich! But news of his wealth soon reached the ears of the emperor, who sent for him. That was when the emperor heard about all that had happened.

The merchant was found, put on trial and made to give half his wealth to the peasant, as he had promised.

That merchant had learned that those who are ungrateful and do not keep their promises always pay in the end.

Gower

1 Noah and the Jackals

from Ethiopia

At the time of the great flood, Noah was checking that all the animals were safe, when he saw two jackals coming towards him.

"Stop!" Noah shouted. "I am sorry, but you cannot come on board my ark!"

"What?" began the jackal, before his wife interrupted.

"All the animals were told that there would be room on board the ark for every living creature, without favour or distinction!" she said, all in one breath. "And if you think you can put us in third class accommodation, you can think again! Surely, it is not asking too much, if –"

"Stop!" Noah shouted again. "You cannot come on board the ark, because, because— this ark is clean and we have no rubbish! And as jackals only eat rubbish and left-overs.."

"Noah!" came a voice from above. "I said *every* creature, and *every* creature it must be! Do not judge living things by what they eat!"

2 The Sheep and the Taxes

Krylov

There was a time when the elephant was made ruler of the forest. And as ruler, he put taxes on this, that and the other, without giving the other animals anything back, or doing anything for them.

And to make matters even worse, the elephant appointed the wolf as Chief of Taxes!

Then, one day, the elephant saw a noticed pinned to a tree.

The notice read, "ALL SHEEPSKINS ARE TO GO TO THE WOLF!"

So the elephant called the wolf and asked him to explain.

"Well," said the wolf, "the sheep pay only small taxes. Yet they are always grumbling, and saying, "that wolf will have the skins off our backs, soon!" So – what else could I do about it?"

"Right!" said the elephant. "We shall take their skins, as they are saying! But woe betide you if you dare touch any of the wool!"

September

3 The Monkeys and the Wild Cat

from Africa

A Wild Cat lay beneath a tree to take a nap – until an ant began crawling through its fur.

"Hey!" he cried to a monkey. "Can you look and see what is crawling over my back?"

The monkey found the ant and took him back to his ant-hill. Then he returned to the cat, expecting a nice "Thank you!" But the cat was already asleep!

The monkey decided to get his own back. He wound the cat's tail around the tree, then ran off to get his friends. Together, they hid in a bush, trying not to laugh as the cat woke up.

The cat pulled its tail this way and that to free itself, but it took a long time and a lot of hard work before he could undo the knot! How the monkeys laughed at him!

By the time he got back to his lair, the cat was so angry! "Five days from now," he told the kittens as he bathed his tail, "tell everyone I'm dead and in my will I asked all the animals to come to my funeral!"

So that is what the kittens did. And on the fifth day, all the animals came to the funeral. But as the monkeys came near, the "dead" cat jumped on them and they ran off, climbing the nearest tree and hiding among the leaves.

And from that day, monkeys have spent most of their lives among the high branches of trees.

4 Two Oxen and an Axle

Aesop

Two oxen were pulling a wagon as big as a house.

All at once, they heard a sound. *Cri-Cri! Cri-Cri!*

"Is there a cricket on my horn?" asked one ox.

"No!" said the other. "That's the axle creaking! It wants us to think this wagon is worn out, so we'll stop working!"

Do you pretend to be tired, when you want to do nothing?

5 The Unbeatable Horse

Twain

There was once a man who owned a horse with such a sorrowful face that all the other horses felt sorry for him. So they always let him take the lead in a race. No wonder that horse with the sorrowful face was always first past the winning post!

It was some time before the other horses learned their lesson – never be fooled by appearances!

6 The Tibetan Yak

Melegari

In the mountains of Tibet lives the yak. It is similar to the ox, and when it calls another yak, it grunts rather like a pig. If a female yak responds, a baby yak may be born some months later. This grunts like a piglet, too, and grows a long, thick coat as it gets bigger, like its parents.

Now, the son of a Tibetan peasant had gone to work in a nearby village – near enough, so that on a summer's evening, his parents could wish him good-night by waving a towel. And he would wave a sheet for them to see. But this was not possible in winter.

So the peasant taught his son to communicate in an ancient Tibetan way, making knots in the long hair of the yak, following a special code. A pat on the rear sends the yak off to where his son lives. The son can then read the message, and send the yak back with an answer in the same way.

7 The Bald Man and the Horse Fly

Fedro

One summer's evening, a bald man felt something sting him, and – slap! – down came his hand on his head.

"Aieee!" screamed a horse fly. "You would kill a living creature for a little sting like that? What did I do to deserve such a slap?"

"I did not mean to harm you," said the man, "but your friends who suck people's blood when they are asleep!"

September

8 The Snail and the Ant

Martin Piaggio

"Why work so hard?" a snail asked some busy ants. "We could all do less! Me, for example, I don't whistle or sing and I move with hardly a sound. My eyes can see all around, and I have on my back a perfect hiding place! What is to stop me becoming a thief and living off the backs of others?"

"The trail which you always leave behind you!" said one of the ants.

9 The Sheep Dog and the Wolf

Gay

A sheep dog had been doing his best to keep the wolf away. But with all the work he had to do on the farm, he could not watch all the sheep all the time.

Then the wolf got to know when the dog had to leave the flock. And after that, there was no peace.

Then one day at sunset the dog went to the wolf's lair.

"Let us talk things over," said the dog. "How is it that a strong, fearless animal like you can attack weak creatures like sheep? Why not choose opponents as strong as you are, like the lion or the wild boar?"

"Friend," answered the wolf, "I am an animal of prey, a hunter by nature. But you speak on behalf of your master. And what you forget is that for every sheep a wolf eats, man eats a thousand! At least I am an enemy which those sheep you guard can recognise!"

10 The Magpie and the Raven

Krylov

A magpie chattered away to a raven, flitting from one branch to another, perching here, flying there.. The raven sat silently, not really paying attention.

"Well?" squawked the magpie at last. "Don't you believe what I am telling you?"

"Well!" answered the raven. "You've been chattering so much that a few lies must have crept in somewhere!"

11 The Fox and the Crab

Eliano

A fox went down to the sea and picked up a stone, holding it tightly under the water.

"That looks good!" thought a crab. "I must have a bite!" It tried using its nippers to tear the stone. "Putting up a fight, eh?" it gasped. "I'll break you, yet!"

And – down came the fox's paw, breaking the crab's shell with the stone. That's what he got for acting too hastily.

12 The Fly Coachman

de la Fontaine

In days gone by, some people travelled long distances by horse-drawn stagecoach. One day, a team of horses were pulling a stagecoach up a steep hill, when a fly landed on the back of one of them.

The fly began buzzing in the ears of one horse, landing on the nose of the other, and flying around the driver – not bothering to notice that the passengers had all got out to push the coach, helping the horses to get it to the top. The fly was still buzzing around when the coach was at the top of the hill and the passengers had got inside.

"Good thing I worked hard!" it buzzed at the horses. "Otherwise the coach would still be down in the valley!"

Some people are like that fly. They go around making a lot of fuss and noise and thinking they are important. But instead of doing anything useful, they are only a nuisance.

13 The Hunter and the Ferret

Yriate

A hunter was showing a friend some rabbits he had caught, proud of being a perfect shot.

But he said nothing of the sugar lump with which he had bribed a ferret to drive the rabbits from their warren, terrorising them and wearing them out in front of the rifle.

"And," the ferret thought to itself, "people say that I'M the enemy of wild rabbits!"

14 The Horse and the Stable Lad

Tolstoy

A young stable lad who had the job of looking after a very handsome horse, sold some of its oats. But he still brushed the animal with great care and groomed him each day. And each time, the lad said, "You're beautiful!"

"I would be even more beautiful," said the horse one day, "if you were only a stable lad and not a dealer in oats!"

15 Mother Nature and the Ewe

Lessing

Mother Nature wanted to help a young ewe to be a stronger animal. "Shall I give you sharp teeth?" she asked.

"No, thank you!" the ewe answered. "I do not want to be like the beasts of prey, such as the fox or the wolf!"

"A poisonous bite!" suggested Mother Nature. "What do you say to that?"

"Oh, no!" said the sheep. "Everyone hates snakes with poisonous bites!"

"All right!" said Mother Nature. "What about a lovely pair of strong horns?"

"But I don't want horns like the cow!" said the sheep.

"I could let you grow them just as you wanted!" Mother Nature went on. "You could use them to protect yourself!"

"I am happiest as I am," said the sheep at last. "If an animal is strong, it is right to use its strength. And I think is better to suffer injustice, than to commit it."

16 The Finch and the Bat

Aesop

At night, a black and yellow finch sang in its cage as if it were still day.

"Why do you sing at night?" squeaked a bat.

"I was caught when I sang by day!" said the finch. "Now I take care to sing only at night!"

"You should have taken care before getting caught!" said the bat. "It is easy to be wise after misfortune!"

17 The Dinosaur and the Professor

Melegari

A learned professor had been following giant footprints, when suddenly – there, in the flesh, stood a dinosaur!

"Brother!" the professor cried in complete amazement.

"Thank you!" boomed the dinosaur, towering high above, "I AM a male dinosaur!"

"A – a talking dinosaur!" gaped the professor . "What a find! I'll be famous! Awards will be named after me..!"

"Is there a lake nearby?" interrupted the dinosaur.

"Oh, yes!" said the man. "One of the reasons you dinosaurs became extinct was lack of water! But are your bones really full of air? In a recent lecture, a colleague at the University of –"

Thump! Thump! Thump! went the huge steps of the dinosaur as he began tramping away. "Sorry," he said. "I have waited millions of years to put in another appearance! And I cannot spend time chatting!"

18 The Crow and the Wolf

de la Fontaine

A raven had found a lovely cheese. Now, she was taking it back to her nest. Feeling a little tired, she perched on a branch – and along came the fox, wanting to see where the delicious smell of cheese was coming from!

"Good day, my dear raven!" said the fox. "How sleek and elegant you always look! I think maybe we should get engaged to be married!"

"Mmmm!" said the raven, lowering her soft black eyelids. "How you flatter me, Mr. Fox!" With the cheese still in her beak, she could only manage a whisper.

"How thrilled I shall be to hear your beautiful song," the fox went on, "sung just for me!" This was too much for the raven! She wanted to let all the animals hear what she could do! So, she puffed out her chest, opened her beak wide – and down fell the cheese for the fox to take back to his lair!

19 The Crow and the Sheep

Fedro

A crow had jumped on a sheep's back, pecking it in sheer spite.

"Aaah!" bleated the sheep. "If you – aaah! – did the same to dogs – aaaaah! – you would not last long! Have you no pity?"

"Scorn the weak and avoid the powerful," squawked the raven, "and you will live for years!"

"Maybe," said the sheep. "But how will your children be regarded?"

20 The Snakes of the Moon

from Australia

Each night, Balu (as the Maori people in Australia call the moon) appears to those on earth, playing with three snakes, a black, a striped and a viper, all with poisonous fangs. One night, Balu saw some men by a river. "Help me get my snakes to the other bank," she said, "and when you die I shall resurrect you! Otherwise you will stay on earth, like this stone!" And as

Balu threw down a stone, it was swallowed up by the mud.

"But, Balu," said the men, "we are afraid of being bitten!"

So Balu came down to earth, and with the viper around her neck, the black snake wrapped around one arm and the striped snake around the other, crossed the river just the same.

After that, men feared snakes more than ever, killing all they found. But it was no good. Balu had decided that as long as people lived on earth, there would also be snakes.

21 How the Redstart got its name

Melegari

Men did not have to think hard about names for animals. You see – the gnu WAS called the gnu by everyone. The same goes for the duck-billed platypus. And a bird called the redstart got its name from the time one hunter said to another, "That red bird gave me quite a start!" But by then, the redstart had flown back to its nest to share the joke with its chicks!

22 The Kite and the Horse

Aesop

A kite is a bird of prey with a soft, mournful sort of voice, which was once much stronger.

The story goes that the kite tried to copy the sound of a horse neighing. His first try was almost perfect. But he went on, trying to make it better – until he lost his voice for good. Then he knew that it is unwise to attempt something which nature never intended us to do.

23 The Crab and the Monkey

from Japan

Crab and Monkey were once good friends – until the crab found the seed of a persimmon fruit and planted it. In time, a tree grew. When it bore fruit, the crab said the monkey could climb up and pick some.

But the monkey ate the best, sweet persimmon fruit, picking the hardest one to throw down at the crab, knocking him out!

The monkey ran away – but the crab had a son, and when he found his father stunned and the hard persimmon nearby, he guessed what had happened.

Crab's son asked the chestnut tree for the hardest nut. Then he invited Monkey to tea, hid the chestnut by the hot stove – and waited.

And when the monkey went to warm his paws by the stove – *bang!* – went the chestnut, hitting him on the nose!

The monkey went wide-eyed in fright – and that is how it has remained to this day.

24 Mother Hen and her Chicks

Tolstoy

"There is a marten about," Mother Hen told her chicks. "You must all go back into your shells, then I will sit on you, as if you were still being hatched!"

"Will we always have to do this?" asked one chick.

"Oh, yes," said the hen.

"But," said the chick, "how will we learn to face danger when we are grown-up hens?"

25 The Zebra's Coat

Melegari

A young wild ass was lost in the forest. He ran in front of a lion, who wanted to bite it, and the forest seemed to him the best place to save his life. He stayed there for a long time – so long that the rays of the sun, shining down between the branches, covered his coat, making the stripes which we all know.

But – did the sun make the white stripes? Or the black?

26 The Animal Professors

Florian

An owl, a cat, a goose and a mouse lived near a big library with books on every subject.

Soon, the animals became keen students of literature and history and would often meet to talk about things.

Once, they were talking about ancient civilisations. The cat said that no country had ever equalled the knowledge of the ancient Egyptians with their pyramids.

"What about the Ancient Greeks?" asked the owl. "Such refined and learned people! All those temples they built!"

"The Egyptians and Greeks do not compare with the Romans!" the goose put in. "They were the masters of civilisation!"

"Stop!" squeaked the mouse. "The Egyptians worshipped cats as sacred, the Greeks did the same with the owl, and Romans kept geese as valued pets! That's why you said all those things! But I am the one to judge, because I have an open mind!"

27 The Chameleon and the Elephant

from Africa

A chameleon is a lizard which can change colour. One chameleon challenged Elephant to a race, got his friends to line the route, then sat on elephant's tail! Seeing one chameleon after another, and all exactly the same colour, Elephant thought he was losing! But cheats never prosper! At the finishing line, the elephant fell, then took a deep breath, stretched his neck – and won!

28 The Ape and the Mirror

Baldi

An ape was looking at himself in a mirror. "Man is so much more handsome than me," he sighed. "Much cleverer, too!" He sighed again, frowning at his reflection.

Thinking how handsome and clever a man was, the ape suddenly hit out at the mirror in temper. Next minute, there was not just one reflection of his ugly, comical face, but one hundred.

29 The Wolf who was hungry

Afanasjev

A wolf thought he was very clever. And because he was always hungry, he went to eat a horse grazing in a field.

"You cannot eat me!" said the horse. "I have my passport!" (He was a very clever horse.) The wolf did not know what a passport was! "Passport?" he said. "Where is it?"

"Under my hoof!" said the horse. "Look!" And as the wolf bent down, the horse gave him such a kick, then ran off.

"Such behaviour in these parts!" thought the wolf. "I shall try the mountains!"

So he went up a mountain and hunted a sheep. "Go to the bottom and open your mouth," said the sheep. "I'll run down and jump in!"

So, the wolf did as he was told. The sheep ran down, jumped – and butted the wolf on the head, leaving him with nothing more than some loose teeth and an empty stomach!

30 The Two Hares and the Hounds

Yriate

"I'm being chased by two greyhounds!" panted a hare.

"They're bloodhounds!" said another.

"No!" protested the first hare. "They're greyhounds!"

"I say they're bloodhounds!" insisted the second hare.

"They are greyhounds!"

Next moment, the hounds had pounced. Not only time is lost through pointless arguments.

The Bear
and the Squirrel

AT one time in the forest of Mongolia, Bear and Squirrel were good friends. They lived, went hunting and did everything together. Bear caught food for Squirrel as well as himself. And the bear ate half the food which the squirrel found. But the fox had made up his mind to spoil their friendship. "How are you, neighbour?" Fox asked the squirrel one day.

At once the squirrel began chatting happily about himself and the bear. Fox gritted his teeth. He had no friends, because he was always so crafty and tricked everyone.

"Poor Squirrel!" Fox burst out suddenly. "Can't you see that Bear is taking advantage of you?"

"Taking advantage of me?" echoed the squirrel. "How?"

"When the bear goes hunting," Fox went on, "who washes the prey before you eat it?"

"He does!" answered Squirrel.

"And do you know why?" said Fox. "So that he can have the best bits for himself! You only get what is left over! That's why you are so small!"

The fox gave a great sigh and began moving off. "Well, goodbye!" he said. "I can see it is no use saying any more!"

But the squirrel had begun thinking. "Maybe Fox is right. Maybe Bear is tricking me! And I thought he was my friend.."

Next day, Bear and Squirrel set off to pick raspberries. Bear picked some first, then washed them and began to eat. He wondered why his friend was not doing the same.

"Supposing Fox is right?" squirrel was thinking.

Then the two friends found a beehive. Bear opened it, put his nose inside and helped himself to honey. He was cleaning his whiskers by the time he called Squirrel to come and have a taste, too.

Once again, the Bear had served himself first. So, it seemed to the squirrel that Fox was right, after all!

"I'll get him next time!" thought Squirrel, annoyed.

The next day they went hunting and caught a goat. Bear

began pulling the goat towards him, when he felt something crawling on his head.. It was the squirrel! He had climbed up, determined to have the first bite! But the bear, not knowing quite what was happening, let go of the goat and the animal ran off like a rocket!

Next, Bear saw a hare and crept up quietly. Then, once again, the squirrel jumped up, this time between the eyes of the bear. The bear began to think of ghosts and evil spirits and trembled with fright!

The hare got away, too.

By now, the bear and the squirrel were not speaking.

All at once, the bear saw a young wild boar. Bear jumped. Squirrel jumped, too – once again, between the bear's eyes! The bear could not help letting go of the wild boar, and he gave a roar of fury.

"I'll get you!" he raged, beginning to chase the wild boar once more.

Once again, the bear felt something crawling over his back. Blindly, he struck out with one paw. Not being able to see Squirrel, the bear put his five claws right into his friend, clawing the skin off Squirrel's back, from head to tail.

The squirrel just managed to stop himself squealing. As soon as Bear took his claws out, he ran into the forest, jumping from tree to tree, and leaving Bear to capture the wild boar.

"At last!" grunted Bear with joy. "Something good to eat!"

Bear turned to the squirrel. But, of course, Squirrel was no longer by his side. And so the bear went back home alone to wait in vain for his friend. But Squirrel was living in the trees. His wounds healed, leaving five black stripes on his back, in memory of those innocent paws of the friend he had betrayed.

Now the Mongolian squirrel never eats meat. And whenever he sees the bear passing, he hurls down handfuls of nuts in rage. Then as soon as the bear raises his eyes, the squirrel hides among the leaves, trembling all over.

from Mongolia

October

1 The Blackbird and the Blackberry Bush

Leonardo da Vinci

A blackbird once pecked at the fruits of the blackberry bush. The bush complained about the scratches on its bark!

"But Nature has made you to feed me!" the blackbird replied. "And when winter comes, you will dry up and your bark shrink!"

But the branches of the blackberry bush were cut down to make a cage. And who ended up in that cage? A blackbird, twittering with fury!

2 The Heron and the Snail

de la Fontaine

Whilst walking along beside a clear stream, a heron saw some lovely, tasty fish in the water – fat carp, delicious pike. But the heron liked to keep to a strict routine!

"It is not lunch-time, yet!" he told himself.

But when it came to lunch-time, there were no pike or carp in the water, only tench and gudgeon and enough little fish for quite a good feed.

"Such fish are not good enough for me!" said the heron. "I shall come back later!"

But the heron grew hungrier and hungrier – until he found himself returning to the bank where he had seen the tench and the gudgeon. Now, all he could find was one snail, which he gobbled down hungrily.

So – learn from that heron. Do not turn your nose up at something if it is not quite what you want. If you set your sights too high, you may end up with nothing.

3 The Piglet and the Sheep

Aesop

When a piglet found himself among the lambs, he did not mind at all. But when the shepherd picked him up, the piglet wriggled and squealed until the man let him go.

"Be a good animal!" said one of the sheep. "We don't mind the shepherd picking one of us up!"

"Your shepherd only wants your wool!" said the piglet. "But he wants my meat!"

4 The Spider and the Fox

from Africa

The fox was out hunting when the spider called. But the fox cubs were there, so the spider began chatting with them.

"Your mother asked me to stay with you!" he said. "My name is All-Of-You! Can you say that?"

"All-Of-You!" repeated the fox cubs.

"Well done! Now I am going in that corner to spin a web!"

Very soon, the fox came in with a bone for the fox cubs.

"This is for all of you!" he said. "I'll get another for myself!"

When the fox had gone, the spider called from his corner, "Little ones you heard your father say that bone was for me!" And he bit a great chunk of meat from the bone and took it back to the dark corner.

He did this many times, until the poor fox cubs began looking like skeletons!

And all the time, Fox was thinking, "My word! That spider is getting on in the world!"

5 The Ermine Stoat, the Beaver and the Wild Boar

Florian

An ermine stoat, a beaver and a wild boar were on their way to a beautiful country to make their fortunes, when they came across a marsh full of slimy toads and poisonous snakes.

The ermine stoat raised her snow-white paws in horror. "That looks disgusting!" she declared. "I am not going in that filth!"

"Give me fifteen days!" said the beaver. "I could build a bridge across this swamp!"

"Fifteen days?" exclaimed the wild boar. "That is too long! Just watch me, my friends!"

The wild boar dived into the water, butting the toads and the snakes with his fangs. In a few minutes he had reached the other bank, covered with mud but happy to think he was on his way to make his fortune.

So many people give up a task at the first obstacle. Others think of complicated ways of solving a problem. The simplest solution is always best.

6 The Hermit Mouse

Martin Piaggio

A mouse was tired of living with other mice. So he found a dark, deserted kitchen with nothing in it except a piece of dry cheese.

The mouse chewed a hole in the cheese, then went inside, nibbling a medium-size hole, big enough for him to fit into.

At the same time, other mice were dying of hunger. Some of the stronger mice went around trying to find food and new homes and anyone who would help. And that is how they came across the hermit mouse.

"How can you expect a poor mouse like me to help you?" he said, when he heard why they were there. "Having chosen the life of a hermit, I have nothing except my hole in this piece of cheese!" And he went back inside.

The mouse was like people who believe that nobody leads such a hard life as they do. They have no time for anyone else's problems but their own.

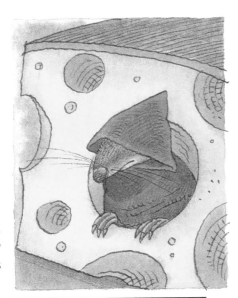

7 The Salmon and the Bear

Melegari

There is a season in the year when salmon go upriver to the mountain streams to lay their eggs. They have to leap up waterfalls, sometimes to be smashed against a stone – and at least one salmon knew what it was to be caught by a bear. "Have I passed 208 metres?" asked the salmon.

"Of course!" growled the bear, not really knowing what the salmon was talking about.

"Hurrah!" cried the salmon. "I have beaten the record for the highest salmon jump! I've won the prize of 100 herrings and a barrel of sea honey! Help me get back in the stream and I'll give you half when I see you again!"

The bear dived with the salmon in its teeth. But he had to drop it because the water went into his mouth, and he was in danger of drowning. At last he reached the bank, in time to see "his" salmon making a jump of two or three metres towards the mountains.

8 The Sparrow and the Grandparents

from Japan

A grandfather had reared a sparrow which flew very well. But the grandmother, his wife, did not like the little bird which flew around the house, pecking at food and sleeping among her stockings. One day, she put it outside the window and waved it away, as if to say, "Go! Go!"

The sparrow was sad and alone, but he did not lose heart. Time passed, and he found a wife and raised a family in a nest in the ruins of an old castle.

One day, the grandfather chanced to come along. The sparrow recognised him and took him to the old castle to meet his wife and children. What celebrations there were!

And when the time came for the grandfather to go home, the bird gave him a kiss and a gold coin which he had found in the castle dungeons.

When she heard about this, the grandmother also went to find the sparrow. He welcomed her as he had welcomed the grandfather, giving her a little chest which was so heavy that she thought it must contain lots of gold coins!

"Here is the key to open it!" said the sparrow. "But not before you get home!"

The grandmother soon hurried home! But when she opened the box – 555 sparrows flew out, flapping and chirping around the house.

If you do not deal properly with problems, they always come back – only ten times worse!

9 The Cheeky Little Goat

Aesop

A little goat had somehow managed to climb up on the roof of the shed.

"Come down," cried the wolf. "Otherwise you could easily slip and fall!" The goat said nothing, so the wolf went on. "Besides, the grass is lovely!"

"You are not inviting me to dinner!" said the cheeky little goat. "You're looking for a meal!"

10 The Frog and the Hen

Yriate

A frog was in the swamp when he heard a hen clucking.

"I've laid an egg!" she told the frog. "So I am telling my master to come and give it to his baby, whilst it is fresh!"

"All that clucking just for one egg?" grunted the frog.

"Better than croaking for hours on end for nothing!" retorted the hen. "Actions speak louder than words!"

11 Animals and Men

de la Fontaine

On a faraway island, a witch transformed into beasts any men who tried landing on the shore. But one man managed to land, thanks to a special drink of his own invention which stopped the witch from turning him into a wild beast, too. This also gave him the power to change the wild beasts back into men.

The lion was not at all pleased when he heard. "I was only an ordinary soldier," he said. "Now I am king of the animals, respected and feared. I shall stay the same as I am!"

The man went to the bear.

"Yes," said the bear, "I was a man, and certainly I was more handsome than I am now! But I married a beautiful she-bear and we are very happy!"

"I do not want to change either!" came a third voice. "I have become a wolf, and I prey on sheep. But I am better than men who are regarded as wolves by other people!"

12 The Pea-Hen and the Farmyard Hen

Lessing

A pea-hen and a farmyard hen were talking. "Your husband, the cockerel sounds important," said the pea-hen, "but men say "Superb!" and "Magnificent!" about my husband, the peacock!"

"People know my husband guards and watches well," said the farmyard hen. "They do not need to notice him. Your husband is only noticed because of his coloured feathers!"

13 The Canary, the Sparrow and the Restaurant

Melegari

A canary once escaped from its cage and flew to the roof-tops. It made friends with a sparrow, who showed the canary where to peck crumbs, under the tables of a luxury restaurant garden.

Here, wonderful meals were served all through the day, and the sparrow fed not only on crumbs but also little tit-bits which people threw to the ground for him.

The canary began pecking timidly among the lovely shoes under the tables. Nobody noticed at first. Then, he became more confident and he began hopping between one table and another.

Then someone caught a glimpse of the canary – and someone else. People looked and the word spread, until the canary was even being shown in the newspapers and on T.V! Then he was fed on delicious food – and put inside a lovely golden cage.

Becoming famous had cost him his freedom.

14 The Wolf and the Tailor

Afanasjev

Going through a wood, a tailor came face to face with a wolf who wanted to eat him! "Can you swallow me?" said the tailor. "Let me measure you!" He took out his tape measure, wound it around the wolf's neck, then his chest, over his shoulders, and – seized his tail with one hand, bringing his other fist down on the wolf's head!

The wolf struggled free – leaving his tail in the man's hand. But seven wolves came in answer to his cries for help, as the man climbed a tree.

The wolves climbed one on the back of another to reach him, the wolf without a tail at the bottom of the column. Just as the seventh was climbing up, the tailor shouted "Watch out! The bear!"

The wolf at the bottom ran off, the others falling to the ground! They were so angry with that wolf without a tail that they chased after him – and the tailor was free!

15 The Coyote Who Flew

from California

The coyote had always admired the hummingbird and the way it flew, like a tiny helicopter.

"How can I fly like you?" he asked the bird one day.

"Just climb a tree and jump!" the hummingbird told him. "The moment before you hit the ground, shout "Up!" and you will rise up! That's more or less what we hummingbirds do!"

The coyote thanked the bird, then climbed the highest tree he could find. "This way, I shall fly for longer!" he thought happily. "And I'll have more time to decide when to shout "Up!" plus more space to rise up into the sky, like the hummingbird does!"

At the top of the tree, he looked down and felt giddy. So he closed his eyes and jumped.

But, with his eyes closed – how could he know when to shout "Up!"? So instead of flying like the hummingbird, the coyote fell to the ground. He never wanted to fly after that!

16 The Hare and the Apple

Clasio

It is nice to give presents. But presents must be given in the right way, as this story shows. It is about a hare who had been searching all day for food. And as night fell, he settled down between the roots of a tree to rest a little.

"At least I might find some fruit," he sighed.

It so happened that he was under an apple tree, laden with fruit which would be ripe the next day. Hearing the hare's words, the tree let an apple fall. *Toc!* It hit the hare right on the head!

The hare thought he was being attacked! He got up and ran away as fast as he could.

Next day, with a great bump between his ears, he came to the apple tree again. "Those lovely apples!" he sighed. "If only I could have one!"

"But I gave you an apple yesterday evening!" hissed the tree. "And you didn't even thank me!"

17 The Eagle and the Water Snake

Cesarotti

One day, an eagle happened to look down and saw a water snake which kept jumping, as if it were trying to bite the eagle. And each time, it fell back to the ground, hissing angrily.

"I understand!" cried the bird. "You are trying to get yourself in my claws, because you want to fly! But those who want something through envy alone, earn only the right to crawl!"

18 The Crossbill and the Pastry Boy

Melegari

A pastry boy had the job of cutting and rolling puff pastry to make biscuits all day long – and each biscuit had to have a hole, right in the middle. It was hard work!

Then one day, the boy saw a lovely crossbill – a bird which feeds on pine seeds, thanks to the top half of its beak crossing over the bottom, like a pair of scissors!

"Try this!" grinned the boy, offering the bird some of the pastry mix. And as the bird pecked out the seeds in the mixture, the boy had the idea of teaching it to peck each piece of puff pastry right in the centre, to make the hole!

This resulted in the boy and the crossbill making a new type of hole for the biscuit – or a new type of biscuit for the hole! Together they became famous all over the world and earned a lot of money!

And after that the crossbill only ever took seeds from pine trees he had already pecked.

19 The Habits of the Frog

Aesop

Mother Frog lived in a pond. Her friend lived in a big puddle by the roadway. "Why not come and live in my pond?" said Mother Frog. "The road is dangerous!"

"I am a creature of habits!" said her friend. But when a vehicle went over her home, she stopped being a creature of habits then.

You can always break a bad habit when you have to.

20 The Two Dogs

de la Fontaine

Two hungry dogs saw an animal in a pond. What a feed, they thought! "Can we swim out and get it?" one dog suggested.

"No," said the other dog. "Let's drink the water to make the pond shallow!"

But they drank so much that they both swelled up and died – like those people who want more and more, until in the end they destroy themselves.

21 The Song of the Lizard

from New Mexico

One day, a fox heard a lizard singing as she lay in the sun. *"Moki, moki, moki, hum!"* He liked the song so much that he begged the lizard to teach it to him. And having such a good ear, the fox soon learned, *"Moki, moki, moki, hum!"*

The fox was still humming to himself, *"Moki, moki, moki, hum!"* when he came to a little pond. Hearing the fox singing, the ducks flew off with such a flutter of wings that the fox quite forgot the lizard's song.

So he went back to the lizard and asked her to teach him, until he could sing once more, *"Moki, moki, moki, hum!"* Then he went on his way.

But soon after, he found himself chasing a hare – and that made him forget the song again!

So he went back to the lizard. And at the entrance to her lair, he found a card, which said, "Closed for the holidays".

22 The Birds and the Net

Tolstoy

Many birds had been caught in a net. But as they were all big and strong, they managed to fly off, taking the net with them.

With each bird wanting to go to its nest, some tried pulling towards the wood, some towards the swamp and some towards the meadows, all pulling against each other. Soon, they fell to the ground, tired to death and the net still around them.

23 The Jackals of Samson

Melegari

In a land called Palestine where the Philistines once lived, there was a type of jackal called the golden jackal. One of the Israelite slaves of the Philistines was a man called Samson.

The story goes that Samson caught 300 golden jackals and tied them in pairs, with a torch-branch between their tails. Then he took the jackals to the Philistine fields of corn, olives and vines, lit each torch-branch, and sent the jackals in.

And as the harvest went up in flames, those golden jackals, torch-branches still burning, knocked on the door of heaven. It was opened by an angel with a sword of fire. Seeing this angel armed in the same way as they who had just burned the harvest, the jackals fled, running all over the sky. And still they run today, trying to find peace and quiet.

That is why the sky at sunset often seems ablaze with fire.

24 The Raven, the Fox and the Wolf

Lessing

A thief had dropped a great piece of meat in the garden of a big house, hoping that the guard-dog would eat it. Instead, a raven had picked it up, nearly choking under the weight!

"You must be the eagle, ruler of the skies!" declared the fox, looking up at the raven and the great piece of meat. "Is that true?"

"Well…" croaked the raven. Too late! He had opened his beak and dropped the meat! But the raven did not seem at all upset to see the fox gobbling it down!

"You wait, Fox!" Raven thought. "You just wait!" In a few moments, the fox began feeling so ill, with such pains in his head that he let out a cry of agony.

The raven had known all along that the thief had poisoned the meat.

But what made it worse for the fox was knowing that a bird could be as cunning as he was!

25 The Squirrel and the Horse

Yriate

From his drey high in a tree, a squirrel often saw a horse going past.

"Don't you get bored, doing the same thing?" he asked one day. "Look at me, going here and there, jumping up the tree, climbing down the trunk –!"

"But," said the horse, "what is the use of all that moving around when you are not running a race?"

26 The Leopard in the Trap

from Africa

A leopard had fallen in a hole which had been dug by game-hunters, then covered with loose soil and branches. First the leopard roared and roared, then began crying for help. But no animals would come to his aid.

"I won't do any more harm to you or any of your kind!" he told the mouse. "I promise!"

The mouse felt sorry for the leopard. He chewed off a long creeper, lowered this into the hole and somehow pulled him out.

By now, the leopard was hungry! "I said you would be spared!" he roared, reaching for the poor mouse. "But that was when I was in the hole!"

"But I have just saved your life!" squeaked the mouse.

"What is wrong?" came the voice of the monkey. "Why all this quarrelling?"

So the mouse and the leopard began telling him the story. "I do not believe it!" cried monkey, when he heard how the mouse had rescued the leopard.

"No?" cried the leopard. "Then I shall show you!" And he went back into the hole.

"See?" he roared, reaching out for the creeper which the mouse had thrown him. Of course, the creeper was not there!

"Aaaargh!" raged the leopard. "Pull me out of here at once!"

"Not likely!" said the monkey. "You have got yourself in a hole. Now you can stay there!"

"That is what you get for being ungrateful!" added the mouse.

October

27 The Great Tit who boasted

Krylov

Seeing the sunset, a great tit told the forest animals how he could set the sea on fire! Next day, they followed him down to the beach! "Fried fish, today!" they cried, each holding a fork in one hand and a lemon in the other.

But, of course, the sea did not burn. And instead of feeling grand, the bird felt stupid for saying something just to impress others.

28 The Fox and the Goose

Lerbs

"How well you swim!" said the fox to the goose. "But can't you come nearer the side of the pond?"

"I think it is best to keep my distance from you!" the goose answered at once.

"Oh, I know that most creatures do not like me!" sighed the fox. "But nobody gives me the chance to be kind and friendly!"

"How sad!" said the goose. She began swimming nearer.

"You geese suffer, too," the fox went on. "Men raise you for your meat, and to fill their cushions with your feathers!"

"I know..." sighed the goose in turn. "But, what can be done?"

"We should form a society!" the fox suggested. "Together, we shall work for our freedom!"

"What must I do?" said the goose, swimming nearer. Next minute... *gobble! gobble!* that fox was enjoying a fine meal!

So beware of taking help from someone you cannot trust.

29 The Hump of the Baby Zebu

Melegari

A zebu is a type of ox with a big hump, and it lives in the east of India.

When a baby zebu is born, it always has trouble getting milk from its mother – because its hump gets in the way!

Luckily, Mother Zebu knows what to do. She lies down on her side, so that her baby can feed – showing us all that for every problem there is a solution.

30 The Donkey and the Lion's Skin

Aesop

A donkey put on the skin of a lion. He looked terrifying as he went out, roaring and stretching his lion's claws, frightening all the animals.

"Now to go and find the fox!" thought the donkey. "He's always playing tricks, thinking he's so clever! Now it's his turn to be frightened!"

Well, the donkey found the fox, and roared like a lion. The fox roared back, and without thinking, the donkey brayed loudly.

Knowing the "lion" was the donkey in disguise, the fox gave chase. And as the donkey ran, the lion's skin began to slip, showing his long nose and yellow teeth, then his ears, then his whole body.

The animals' fear turned to rage, and they chased the donkey, throwing sticks at him! And so the donkey learned that it is always best to be who you really are. And if you are going to play a part, make sure you do not over-act!

31 The Story of the Giant Roc

Arabian Nights

A sailor landed one day on an island where there was an enormous white egg, as big as a great house. This was the egg of the roc, a bird as big as the moon.

The sailor smashed the egg – and found inside a chick which was big enough to fill the whole of the ship's hold!

But as he sailed away, the giant roc saw what had happened! It flew after the ship with a great pounding of its enormous wings, carrying a whole mountain in its claws! And as it hovered above the man, it let the mountain fall.

Using all his strength on the rudder, the sailor swung the ship out of danger. Instead, the mountain fell into the sea, forming a new island off the coast of Africa.

The ship's crew cooked the meat of the bird from the egg. And when they woke next day, the white-haired had black hair, and those who had black found their hair was white.

The Musicians of Bremen

A DONKEY knew that his master wanted to be rid of him when he became too old to work. So he decided to walk to Bremen and become a musician in one of the town bands. Before long he met an old dog, panting by the side of the road.

"I am going to Bremen to become a musician," said the donkey. "Why not come, too?"

"Good idea!" said the dog, and they walked on together.

Soon, they met a poor, old cat. "We are going to Bremen to become musicians!" said the dog. "Why not come, too?"

"All right!" mewed the cat. Presently, they came to a farm, where a cockerel sat on a gate, crowing loudly.

"Why are you crowing?" asked the donkey.

"Well," said the cockerel, "I shall be roasted tomorrow. So if I cannot sing now, when shall I sing?"

"We are going to Bremen to become musicians!" said the cat. "Why not come, too?"

"Thank you very much!" crowed the cockerel. And so the four friends went on together.

It was dark by the time they came to Bremen. The donkey and the dog stretched out under a tree, the cat curled up on a branch, and the cockerel flew to the top. "Look!" he cried. "Just see the moon!"

But it was not the moon. It was the light from the window of a house. So they all got up and went towards it, hoping they might find warmth, food and shelter for the night.

The donkey stretched his long neck and peered inside. "There's a gang of men round the table!" he told the others in a whisper. "They look like bandits to me! And what food they're eating!"

The four friends made a plan. First the donkey put his front hooves on the window sill. Then the dog jumped on his back, with the cat on the dog's back and the cockerel on the cat's head. Then at a signal from the donkey, each one began its own music. The donkey brayed, the dog barked, the cat mewed and the cockerel began crowing!

Still crowing and mewing and barking and braying, they broke

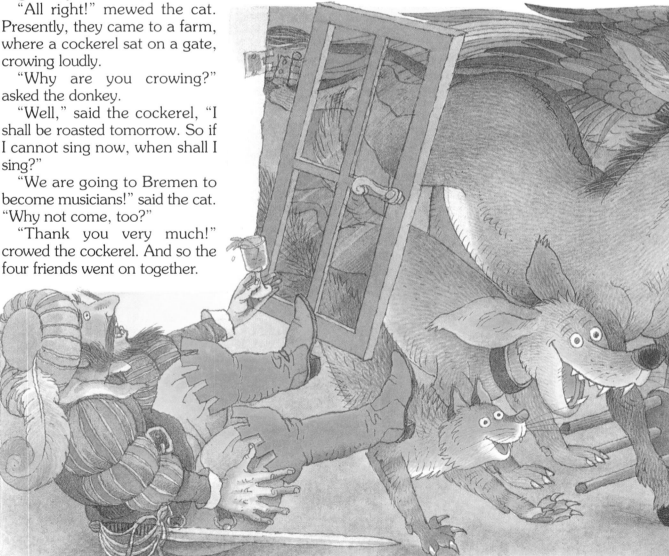

the window and burst into the room, making the bandits flee in terror.

Then the donkey, the dog, the cat and the cockerel sat down at the table and ate all that was left, before settling down for the night. The donkey snuggled down in a bed of hay in the yard, the dog curled up behind the door, the cat lay beside the warm fireplace and the cockerel perched on a wooden beam.

The cockerel put out the candle with the tip of its wing, and all was quiet.

Meanwhile, the bandits were wishing they had not run away. "We must have been dreaming!" the bandit chief told his second-in-command. "Go and take a look!"

So the man went back to the house and crept in. The sharp-eared cat heard his footsteps and opened one eye.

The man thought this was a coal glowing in the fire, and tried to light a taper. This made the cat fly in his face, scratching with all her might!

The bandit gave a cry of pain

and ran to the door, which the dog was guarding. He soon bit the man's leg!

"Urrrgh!" roared the bandit – which woke up the donkey and kicked the man in the back! "Cock-a-doodle-doo!" crowed the cockerel, waking up and thinking it must be daybreak.

Finding it was still night, the bird clawed and scratched in anger. By now, the man could not leave fast enough!

"In that house," he told the bandit chief, "a witch scratched my face! Behind the door, another pulled a knife across my leg! In the courtyard another kicked me with shoes of iron, and on the roof a judge shouted, "Get the robber, do!"

"Then we must go!" cried the bandit chief.

And so the friends became masters of their own house at Bremen, a city famous not only for its music – but also a statue of four animal musicians.

The Brothers Grimm

1 The Hare in the Moon

from China

Look carefully at a full moon, and you may see the Hare of Buddha, founder of a religion with 300,000,000 followers.

The story is that as Buddha lay starving, the hare threw itself on the fire to be eaten. To repay him, Buddha sent his soul to the moon, where he pounds the ingredients of a mixture to make sure that the soul never dies.

2 The Lion and the Gnat

de la Fontaine

"You pest!" roared the lion at the gnat. "Sting me once more and I'll tear you to pieces!"

"In pieces?" laughed the gnat. "You can hardly see me!" And he stung the lion again!

The lion jumped to his feet and gave a roar which echoed through the forest, clawing and scratching at his back, his nose and his neck – whilst the gnat went on biting and stinging wherever it could.

At last, the lion sank to the ground, quite exhausted, beaten by a tiny, little insect.

The gnat buzzed triumphantly for everyone to hear. He was still feeling pleased with himself when he flew straight into a spider's web.

And so this story shows how the great and the strong can often be beaten by a tiny enemy. But there is also an old saying that it is possible to overcome the waves of the ocean, and then drown in a glass of water.

3 The Bulldog and the Tiger Cub

Martin Piaggio

There was a time when all the cats and the dogs in the world wanted peace with each other. And that is how a bulldog went to see a tiger cub who had been an enemy. "It is so nice to be friends!" said the bulldog. "I suppose you are going to cut those long, sharp claws, now!"

"Yes," answered the tiger cub, "when I see that you have cut your long, sharp teeth!"

4 The Leopard, the Fox and the Lion

de la Fontaine

There was once a leopard who, as Sultan of his kingdom, appointed the fox as Prime Minister.

The leopard wanted the fox to find out if one particular lion cub would ever try to get his throne.

"I know just what to do!" said the fox. "I could make friends with the lion's son, watch him as he grows and see all that he does –"

And so the fox went on. But nothing was decided. Whenever the matter was raised, the leopard would just nod his head and say, "Yes… Yes, tomorrow we shall see…"

Well, the young lion grew big and strong. And one day, he went to the palace of the Leopard Sultan. In the place of the fox, he put the throne. And in the place of the Sultan, he put himself – a young lion who believed in the saying – "Never put off until tomorrow anything you can do today!"

5 The Student and the Two Lizards

Yriate

A student of natural history caught two lizards to study. One lizard he killed, so that he could cut it open and examine all the parts under a microscope.

The second lizard felt so lonely. But in time, the student set it free. And how happy that lizard was to return to live among friends!

But soon he began to give himself airs, saying how valuable he had been in the cause of science.

"If man has made me the subject of such great study," he told the other lizards, "we must be important creatures! So it is time to leave these smelly little holes of ours to the spiders, the ants, the scorpions and other insects!"

But none of the other lizards wanted this, and they turned their backs on him.

Once again, the lizard knew how it felt to be all alone. But this time, he had only himself to blame.

6 The Tail of the Donkey

Guerrazzi

A man worked his donkey so hard that one terrible day, the poor beast fell as he entered the city, weighed down by sacks of potatoes, baskets of melons and bottles of wine.

But instead of unloading the donkey a little and helping him to get up, the man asked a passer-by to pull the donkey by the tail, whilst he pulled at the head.

"Right?" cried the man, grabbing the donkey's nose.

"Right!" nodded the passer-by, holding tight to its tail.

Together they pulled and pulled, trying to get the poor donkey to its feet. Suddenly, the passer-by lurched back, the donkey's tail in his hand!

"You have ruined my animal!" shouted the man. "I'll see you pay for this!"

And in reply, the passer-by slapped the man in the face with the donkey's tail. The owner of the donkey took the man to court, where a judge heard what each of them had to say. Then he gave sentence. "The passer-by will become joint owner of the donkey," said the judge, "until the animal grows its tail again! Only then will the animal be able to work. Only then will it belong to the man once more!"

"But, Your Honour," cried the man, "nobody has ever seen a donkey grow back its tail!"

"That is true," said the judge. "So each day you will be reminded of what you both did to that poor animal!"

7 The Mosquito and the Bull

Aesop

A mosquito had eaten a meal. He landed on a bull's horn, staying still to help his food digest. After a while, he said to the bull, "I am going now! Sorry if I disturbed you!"

"I didn't hear you come," said the bull, "and I shall not feel it when you go!"

That bull could have been speaking about people who do nothing worthwhile.

8 The Bee, the Sheep and the Man

Lessing

A bee was proud the farmer liked her honey! "Which animal is most useful?" she asked him.

"The sheep!" said the farmer. "Its wool is so soft and warm!"

"Sheep?" echoed the bee. "But what about my honey?"

"That is always welcome!" said the farmer. "But a sheep can be sheared without any trouble! We always risk a few stings collecting your honey!"

9 The Condor and the Bull

Melegari

At one time men arranged fights between condors and bulls. Just before one of these fights, a bull spoke to a chaffinch who was pecking at the flies on his horns.

"Go to the condor," he said. "Tell him to put his ear to the ground as soon as he sees the setting sun touch the horizon. Then he can send me back a message with his beak!"

At sunset, the bull beat out a message on the ground with his horns. The sound reached the ear of the condor, and the bird tapped his beak on the ground in reply.

Next day, the fight began with the condor seizing the bull's horns in its great claws. It spread its wings, lifting the bull, then dropping together on the table of food spread for the cruel people who had come to see one animal kill another. Then the bull and the condor went off together into the forest, where nobody bothered them ever again.

10 The Australian Cockerel

from Australia

The Australian cockerel crows like no other cockerel. And the story goes that if anyone or anything tries to copy him, he is so offended that he does not sing any more. And if he does not sing, then the sun does not rise. And if the sun does not rise, it will always be night.

So, if you ever do meet an Australian cockerel – remember to treat him with respect!

11 The Fox and the Scarab Beetle

Aesop

All the animals agreed Fox was clever. If only, they said, he would use his brains well, instead of playing tricks and doing harm!

Perhaps, said Mother Nature, if she made Fox king, he would have to act with dignity and behave himself.

Fox was pleased, especially when he got a fine carriage with satin cushions and the royal crown painted on the door!

One day, he was giving orders to his driver and footman, when a scarab beetle got inside and began buzzing under his nose. Fox, quite forgetting himself, began grabbing here and reaching there, inside and outside the carriage, shouting and bawling, trying to catch it.

That was when Mother Nature knew Fox could never be king! Away went the carriage, the crown, the driver and the footman. And the fox once again became – just the fox!

12 The Ugly Duckling

Hans Andersen

Mother Duck's eggs had all hatched, except one.

"It must be a turkey's egg!" said a friend. "Throw it in the pond!"

But the duck continued to sit on the egg, until one day – *c-crack!* – the egg opened, and out came an ugly little duckling with grey feathers.

The duckling began to grow. But because he was so ugly, he had no friends. One day, as he heard the sound of guns, a dog came and sniffed at him. He thought the duckling was so ugly that he left him there!

And so the ugly duckling ran away, towards a far-off lake. Somehow, by eating whatever he could, and finding shelter here and there, he managed to last the cruel winter. And when spring came and the pond was as blue as the sky, he saw himself in the water.. a bird with a slender neck and lovely white feathers!

The ugly duckling had become a beautiful swan!

13 The Rich Cockerel and the Poor Cockerel

from Micronesia

On a distant island there lived a rich cockerel with gold spurs on his legs. Every morning he sang in his superb voice. Then one day, he had barely finished his song when another cockerel began. "Another cockerel who sings like me?" the rich cockerel thought. "Can it also be that he is richer than I am?"

He walked towards the sound of the crowing, and saw a cockerel like him, but with no golden spurs on his legs.

"Why are you copying my song?" he crowed. "Are you making fun of me?"

"There is no other song like my crowing!" answered the poor cockerel. "And no song is more or less important than any other!"

The rich cockerel was silent for a moment, thinking about the poor cockerel's words. "You are right," he said at last. "No creature should be seen as being better than another. Let us be friends!"

14 The Panda and the Bamboo

Melegari

The first panda arrived in Europe in 1930. The directors of a zoo looked him up and down, trying to decide what to call him.

"Welcome, dear – er, dear –"

"Pei-hsiung!" said the panda. "That is my name in Chinese!"

"But," spluttered the director, "we cannot put "Pei-hsiung in Chinese", outside your cage, can we?"

"But what can I do?" said the new arrival. "I can only say that I come from the Xsifan mountains, and eat only bamboo! Italian students call this my "pane", meaning "bread". They call out "Pan-da-Bambu!" when they come to feed me!"

"Right!" cried the director. "We shall shorten that to "pan-da"!"

How the panda got its name may be just a story. But it was only introduced to Europe in 1930. It does come from the Xsifan mountains. Its name is Pei-hsung in Chinese. And it eats only bamboo shoots.

15 The Cow and the Goat

Tolstoy

A farmer had a cow and a goat. When the cow mooed he gave her a loaf to eat, to keep her still.

One evening, the goat came and stood in front of the farmer and the cow. The farmer hit her to make her move.

"If the cow stays still, she gets food!" the goat bleated. "I stay still and get beaten! It's not fair!" She butted a pail with her horns, and fresh milk spilt all over the floor.

16 The Mouse from the Plain & the Mouse from the Country

Tolstoy

A mouse who lived on the plain met another who lived on a mountain and they promised to visit each other. The mouse from the plain climbed the mountain, admiring the view, thinking how pure the air was and how fresh the grass smelt.

"When do we eat?" he asked.

"Right now!" came the voice of the Wild Cat – and ate up the mouse from the mountain.

"Where do you come from?" the cat asked the other mouse.

"Th-the plain!" he stammered. "Lots of mice live there!"

"Take me there!" said the cat. "Sit on my head and let us go!"

When they got to the plain, the mouse pointed to the cover of a drain. "This is the door to where all the mice live!" he said.

"Underground?" mewed the cat. "Up in the mountain it is MUCH safer!" But, somehow, the mouse from the plain could not agree.

17 The Lion, the Eagle and the Bat

Yriate

"The bat cheats us all!" Eagle told the lion. "It can fly, so it says it is a bird! It also pretends to be a mouse, because it squeaks like them! AND he smells like garlic!"

In the end, the lion had to stop the bat going out by day. Now he only goes out at night. And instead of perching on branches like birds, the bat hangs upside down, wherever it is.

18 The Turtles and the Flamingos

Firenzuola

Rain had not fallen for months. Now, a lovely blue rain-pond had become a sea of mud.

A pair of flamingos who lived on the banks of the pond decided to fly away to find another home. Before leaving, the two birds went to see their neighbour, the turtle.

"You are lucky to be able to fly!" he sighed. "When you get to your new home, think of me!"

"I know how we can take you with us!" said one flamingo at last. "We will fly alongside each other, holding a long stick in our beaks. Then you can hold on to the stick with your mouth!"

"Thank you, my friends!" cried the turtle. "You can be sure I will keep my mouth tightly shut all through the flight!"

The idea was put into action. The flamingos found a stick, the turtle grabbed hold of the centre with its mouth, then with a flamingo holding the stick at either end, the flight began.

With the weight they were carrying, the two birds had to fly low. This meant that all the other animals saw the flying turtle!

"What are you doing up there?" one cried.

"You do look funny!"

"Don't bump into the clouds!"

It went on and on, until the turtle could take no more. He opened his mouth to shout back – and fell *splash!* into lovely, clear water

He and the flamingos had found their new home at last.

19 The Vain Donkey

Clasio

When a donkey was loaded with stale cheese, people kept their distance as he went by!

"Everyone gets out of my way!" he thought. "I must be important!"

Next day, he was loaded with flowers and people came to enjoy the scent! "I have so many admirers!" Donkey cried.

"It's not you," said a dog, "but what's on your back!"

20 The Jackal Among The Stars

Melegari

An astronomer had been reading about jackals. "The jackal does not kill," he thought. "It eats food which others leave. So why is it despised? I must do something!"

With his telescope he found three stars without a name.

He called them Jackal 1, Jackal 2, and Jackal 3 – after the animal who follows the great meat-eaters of the deserts.

21 The Wolf and the Grandmother

Aesop

A hungry wolf was prowling around! Suddenly he heard the cry of a child. Then came the voice of a grandmother. "Stop that!" she scolded. "I'll get the wolf to come and eat you!"

"Oooh!" thought the wolf, licking his lips.

An hour passed, then another. Night fell, and the wolf was still there, waiting for the grandmother to call him.

"Time for bed!" he heard her say. "Put the light out and go to sleep!"

"What about the wolf?" asked the child.

"Don't worry!" said the grandmother. "If he comes here, I'll hit him with my stick!"

"What is she talking about?" wondered the wolf. "How can you trust people who say one thing, and do something else?"

For once, the wolf was right. What people end up doing is often not the same as what they say they will do.

22 The Ferret and the Fox

Krylov

The ferret likes catching rabbits. One day, escaping from a rabbit keeper, he ran into his lair, just as the fox came along. "I could do with some words of comfort," said the ferret. "Do you think I am a thief?"

"No!" Fox exclaimed. "You must have something on your conscience!" And it is true. A dishonest action always leaves a mark of unease.

23 His Majesty, the Hummingbird

from Celebes

The hummingbird may be small, but he is one who brought to earth a piece of the sky! That was the task set by the eagle, the peacock, the pheasant and the falcon to find a king over all the birds.

Before the contest, the hummingbird slid something under his wings. Then, making sure no other bird was nearby, he flew on to the falcon's back.

Well, no bird could bring back a piece of the sky. One by one, they returned to earth, almost tired to death.

But the hummingbird flew up and up on his own. And when he returned to earth, there was something sparkling in his slender beak. "It is a piece of the sky," he said. But the others did not believe him and did not make him their king.

Was it because he was small? Or – had someone seen him flying on the falcon's back and hiding something under his wings?

24 The Chamois Deer and Friends

de la Fontaine

A mouse, a tortoise, a raven and a chamois deer always met at mealtimes. One day, the deer was late. It was the raven who found him in the net of a game-hunter.

The raven fetched the mouse and together they went to the rescue, telling the tortoise to stay where she was.

But the tortoise wanted to help, too. And just as she came to the place where the raven and the mouse had chewed away at the net and set the chamois deer free, the hunter arrived, very angry.

"Right!" he shouted. "You can pay for all of them!"

He had tied the poor tortoise in a sack, when the chamois deer appeared again. The hunter dropped the sack and began chasing him.

This gave the raven and the mouse chance to chew the sack and free the tortoise.

And when evening came and they were back together, what celebrations there were!

25 What the Kite had for Lunch

de la Fontaine

Seeing a plump little mouse at the side of the pond, a frog called out to him.

"There are better things to do than just walking, Master Mouse! Come and see how things are with us water creatures!"

The mouse accepted the frog's invitation at once. He was no expert at swimming, so the frog tied him to a reed and towed him along by the stem.

When the frog reached the middle of the pond, he changed his tune. "You've had it now! I'm going to drop you to the bottom of the pond, so you can feed all my little frogs!"

"No, no!" squeaked the mouse, trying to pull away, back towards the bank. At the same time, the frog tried to pull him further into the pond. A kite saw all this. He dived into the pond, seized the reed in his beak and pulled up the mouse and the frog together, thinking what a good feed he would have.

26 The Fox and the Turkeys

de la Fontaine

A crafty fox had come across a flock of plump turkeys. How he wished he could eat a few! But the birds always kept guard, watching the fox every hour of the day and night.

But instead of giving up, the fox kept thinking what he could do.

One moonlit night, he went to the tree where the turkeys were keeping guard, their eyelids heavy for want of sleep.

"Ladies and gentlemen!" he announced. "Some special entertainment in your honour!" And he began walking on his front paws, waving his tail in the air, dancing and leaping about, knowing that they dare not take their eyes off him.

The turkeys watched the fox, until they fell out of the tree, quite exhausted. And as each one fell, so he picked it up to take back to his den.

Whenever you are frightened of something, the more likely you are to be beaten by it.

27 The Hen and the Chicken

Lessing

There was once a hen who could not see very well. But she pecked around just the same as when she was young, putting her head near the ground to find the smallest seeds, insects and earthworms – which a lazy, young chicken often pecked without a word of thanks.

Those who make a habit of copying from others are like that chicken, lazy enough to pick the brains of others.

28 How the Camel got his Hump

Rudyard Kipling

When the horse, the dog and the ox began working for man, the camel only lazed about in the desert, eating whatever it could find, and answering anyone with a short *"Humph!"*

Presently, a horse came to find him. "Camel," said Horse, "come and trot with us!"

"Humph!" said the camel.

Then a dog came to see him, a stick in its mouth. "Camel," said the dog, "come and fetch sticks like the rest of us!"

"Humph!" said the camel. He said the same thing to the ox, when he came to ask for some help with the ploughing.

"If the camel will not work," man said, when they told him, "you three must work harder!"

The horse, the dog and the ox were wondering what to do, when there came a great rush of air and sand. And in the centre was the *Djinn* (or spirit) of All the Deserts. When he heard about the beast who would not work, he said, "We'll see about this!" and went to see the camel. And at the first *"Humph!"* he gave the camel a "hump" of his own, right on his back!

"Well," said the camel, "I cannot work now!"

"Why not?" asked the Djinn. "You missed three days' work. So in that hump is enough energy to keep you going for three days without eating!"

And so the camel went to work, and still works hard to this day, taking people across the desert sands.

29 The Fish-Bird and the Little Girl

from the New Hebrides

A little girl was drawing water from a woodland spring, when she saw in the water such a brightly coloured creature!

"Are you a bird?" she called. "Or a fish?"

"Ha-ha-ha!" came the reply.

The girl put her hand in the water and the fish-bird swam away. But when she put her hand back, there it was again.

The little girl took her pail and began emptying the water, pouring it on the ground. But the fish-bird was still there. Then, as she emptied the last bucketful, the strange creature vanished.

The girl scratched her head, and with a long face, upturned the bucket and sat on it.

"Why do you look for me down there," said a voice, "when I am up here?"

The girl lifted her eyes. Then she understood. There on the branch of a tree sat a beautiful parrot. It was his reflection she had seen in the water!

30 The Greedy Man, the Cook and the Owl

from Africa

A rich man was planning an important dinner. "Cook!" he said. "We shall have roast goat with raisins! I want to make a good impression!"

But as she returned to the kitchen, the man sent for her again. "On second thoughts," he said, "lamb might be best."

The cook had not gone far, when the man called yet again.

"Do you think," he said, not looking at her face, "a pair of cats would be enough?"

The cook was so horrified, she could not speak. "You agree!" said the man. "That is what we shall have!"

The cook went back to the kitchen, as white as a sheet. She told her husband about it, and he knew that among the guests was a wizard. Hearing what the man planned to do, the wizard changed him into an owl with one wing longer than the other, so that he would always remember and regret being mean instead of generous.

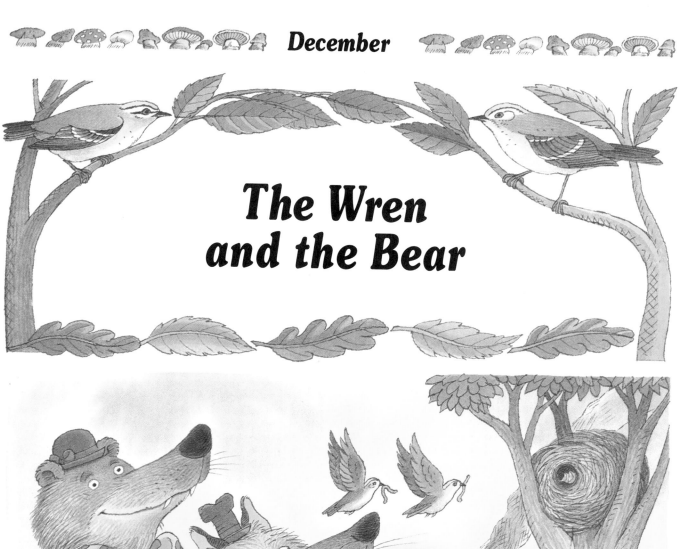

The Wren
and the Bear

ONE day the bear and the wolf were out together, when the bear heard a bird singing.

"Wolf," he said, "what is that bird who sings so well?"

"It's the king of the birds!" said the wolf – although the bird was only a little wren. "We must bow if we see him!"

"Ooh!" said the bear. "Can we go to see his palace?"

"Not yet," Wolf said. "Wait until the queen comes back!"

Just then, the queen flew past the two animals along with the king, both with food in their beaks for the chicks. Of course, the bear wanted to follow them. "No," Wolf said. "Wait until the king and queen have flown away again!"

They went on a little way, but still the bear wanted to see the royal palace. So, back he went. And the moment he saw the birds flying off, he went and peeped inside the nest.

This was quite hard to do. The wren's nest was like a big ball of mud, twigs, leaves and suchlike, with a tiny, round entrance, only a little bigger than the eye of the bear! But somehow, he peeped inside and saw five or six baby wrens.

"This is the royal palace?" he cried. "What a dump! You are no children of a king, but common little brats!"

"No we are not!" the wrens burst out together. "You take back all that you have said!"

"Hah!" grunted the bear. "I could frighten you to death if I wanted!"

And off he went to tell the other animals all about the miserable place where the king of the birds was living.

By this time, the king and queen had flown back to their nest. And when they heard how the bear had spoken to their children, they went to see him.

"Bear!" cried the king, loud enough for everyone to hear. "You have insulted us wrens! We must declare war!"

All the flying animals, birds both big and small, bats and flying insects such as the bees, the wasps, mosquitoes and gnats went on the side of the wrens. All four-footed animals, like the bull, the donkey and the horse

went on the side of the bear, with Fox in command.

"We shall march into battle with me at the head of the column!" said the fox. "If I keep my tail straight up, you must keep marching. But if you see my tail hanging down, that means we are surrounded by the enemy, and then you must all escape at once!"

And so came the day of the battle. All the four-footed animals marched to the battle-field, their heavy footsteps making the ground shake beneath them.

The wrens' army arrived with a loud flutter of wings and enough buzzing and whirring and humming and crying to frighten any enemy.

And so the two armies advanced, one against the other.

Seeing the fox at the head, King Wren sent for the hornet.

"I want you to hide in the tail of the fox!" he ordered. "Then get ready to sting him!"

When the fox felt the first sting, he gave a jump – but he kept his tail upright.

But on the second sting, he let his tail fall without thinking, just for a second.

And at the third sting, he could not stop his tail dropping between his legs!

When his army saw this, they thought they were surrounded by the enemy! They began to run here and there, trying to get away back to their dens and their lairs as soon as they could.

When it was all over, the king and the queen went back to their nest. "Children!" they cried. "We have won the war! Now you can eat and drink as much as you like!"

But still the wrens were not happy. "We will not eat," they said, "until the bear has begged our pardon, and called us Your Royal Highnesses!"

And when he received the message, the bear went to the wrens' royal palace and begged their pardon and called the baby wrens their Royal Highnesses. And their Royal Highnesses smiled and chirped now that they knew they were respected by all.

The Brothers Grimm

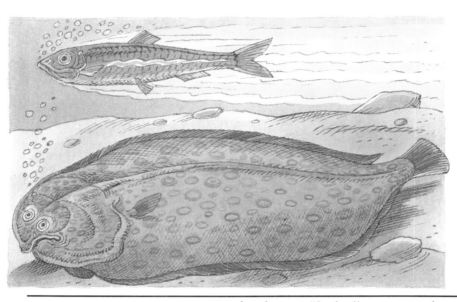

1 The Jealous Sole

Grimm

All the fish in the ocean decided that their king should be the one who swam the fastest. So, they got into a line, and the race began. Soon, there came a cry, "Herring has won!"

"Who?" asked the sole, not sounding at all pleased. "That titchy fish?" and the mouth of the sole curled up into such a sneer that it is still crooked to this day.

2 The Eagle and the Scarab Beetle

Aesop

The Greek god Zeus always admired the eagle, so fierce and strong. But the most important creature a poor hare knew was the scarab beetle. So when he found himself being chased by the eagle, he turned to the scarab beetle for help. The scarab beetle bravely flew to the eagle, begging him not to harm the hare. But the great creature took no notice and gobbled up the hare. "I shall get you for this!" thought the beetle. And it began hiding in the eagle's nest, ready to make the eggs roll outside and fall to the ground.

In the end, the eagle was in such despair that it went to see Zeus. And the king of the gods, understanding how serious this was, said that Mother Eagle could lay her eggs in his own lap.

When the scarab beetle got to know, it made a great ball of mud, dried worms and bits of dirt, pressing it all together with its feet. Then it flew above the lap of Zeus and dropped the ball.

And as Zeus jumped up to shake off the horrible mess, the egg fell to the ground. The eagle knew why all this had happened. She returned to her nest – and now the eggs of the eagle are laid at the time when scarab beetles do not mate. This fable tells us that nobody need despair of being bullied. Even the weakest among us can find ways of paying back those who do us harm.

3 The Spider and the Silk Worm

Martin Piaggio

A spider was watching a silk worm spin its cocoon. "Why do you work so slowly?" it asked. "I spin my web in half an hour! You take about ten days to spin a badly shaped cocoon in which to hide yourself!"

"I spin silk," the silk worm answered. "You spin a web to trap flies!"

Quality is always more valuable than quantity.

4 The Boy and the Lion

Aulo Gellio

As a lion went hunting in the forest, a thorn stuck in his paw and made his foot swell. The lion began suffering so much that his cries of pain were heard by a young boy. At first, he was too afraid to come near. But, knowing that the great beast needed help, at last managed to get near enough to pull the thorn out. Then he helped the lion reach a cave, where he could rest.

The boy was a slave who had escaped from a cruel master. At this time, slaves who were re-captured were thrown to the lions in an open air arena, as entertainment for the people.

But when the boy was caught and taken to the Roman arena, he found himself facing the lion he had helped!

The beast recognised the boy at once, and, instead of attacking him, went and sat at his feet.

This was seen as a sign from the gods. The boy was thought a great hero and made a free man.

5 The Wolf and the Badger

from Caucasia

"I am going to eat you!" said a wolf to a badger.

"What about my prescription?" asked the badger. "Without that, I stay in the stomach for a year, a month and a day!"

"Get it, then!" said the wolf.

"But," said the badger, "you must jump three times, and shout hurrah!"

But, by the second "hurrah!" the badger was far away!

6 The Frogs who wanted a King

de la Fontaine

The frogs in a great pond decided that they needed a king. First they asked softly. Then they asked loudly. Until down from the sky came their king. It was a log of wood.

As it thudded into the deep mud, the frogs went and hid. But seeing that it did nothing but stay afloat, they began going nearer and nearer, then touching it, then climbing on its back and jumping over it.

"What king is this?" said one of the frogs at last. "He does not rule over us or command respect!"

"That is right!" agreed another. "We need a real king!"

So the mighty god Jupiter sent them a crane, a wading bird who liked to catch frogs in its long beak and eat them.

But those frogs had only themselves to blame. It would have been so much better to have kept to their own way of life, or to keep a king who was gentle and kind and did them no wrong.

7 The Cricket who loved the Parrot

Melegari

At the foot of a willow tree, beneath the nest of a cricket, a poor man often sat, holding out his cap to passers-by. He had a parrot and a collecting tin. And when anyone threw a coin into the man's hat, the parrot would pick it up and put it in the tin with a loud *ting!* People often threw more coins, just to watch the parrot and hear *ting! ting!*

The cricket soon fell in love with the beautiful bird. But he was never brave enough to speak to her.

Winter came and the man no longer held out his hat for money – he needed it to keep his head warm. He hardly went out, neither did the parrot.

But the cricket stayed under the willow tree, dreaming of his love and the *ting! ting!*

That is why the song of the cricket sounds like the *ting! ting!* of the coins falling in the collecting tin. And all for a parrot who never knew how much he loved her!

8 The Hare and the Cabbages

de la Fontaine

A farmer had a lovely field of cabbages, protected by a thick hedge. All the same, a hare began coming and eating them secretly. So the farmer sent for the best hunter in the district, offering the man as many cabbages as he could carry if he could shoot the hare.

The hunter lost no time. He went into the field of cabbages with a pack of dogs.

But that cabbage field was vast, with rows and rows of cabbages, all the same size, shape and colour. Looking for that hare was like searching for that famous needle in a haystack!

Then suddenly, the hunter caught sight of a cabbage with long ears – the long ears of the hare, hiding behind it!

"There!" shouted the hunter to his dogs.

And there began a terrible destruction – not of the hare, but of cabbages!

The dogs, following the orders of the hunter, ran among the cabbages with shots whistling all around, and dust being raised by so many feet scampering here and there. In the end, that field of cabbages looked like a battlefield – and all for the sake of one hare!

And as that hare was going back into his lair, safe and sound, the hunter was talking to the farmer.

"Best mend the holes in that hedge," he advised, "before that terrible hare comes back!"

9 The Horse and the Bull

Lessing

A horse galloped across a field, carrying a boy about ten years old. He rode bareback, without saddle or bridle, stirrups or reins, guiding the horse by holding its mane.

A bull shouted across to the horse. "Aren't you ashamed of being ridden in that way by a boy? I would never allow it!"

"But what is the point," said the horse, "of making him fall?"

10 The Rabbit and the Frogs

Aesop

A rabbit was so sad at being shy and timid that he decided to end his life. He ran to the deepest pond he knew – but as he reached the side, he saw hundreds of frogs swimming away in fright.

"So," he thought, "there ARE some creatures more timid than me!" He turned away happily, already looking forward to a nice, juicy carrot!

11 The Great Serpent and the Moon

from Sumatra

At the time when the earth was thought to be flat and people could fall off the edge, a shepherd was caught in a heavy shower of rain.

He sheltered under some trees, not knowing he was at the entrance to the home of the Queen of the Serpents – until she attacked him.

In defence, the man threw stones, breaking an egg which was curled up in the monster's tail. With the serpent at his heels, the shepherd ran and ran, until he came to the ends of the earth. "Moon!" he cried. "Please, save me from the great serpent!"

The moon did not hesitate. "Let the shepherd go," she said to the Great Serpent. "And you can eat me every month!" And that is why the moon every twenty eight days becomes almost invisible, when, so this old story goes, she is swallowed up by the Great Serpent.

12 Animals in Dreams

Kafka

In a dream, a wise man saw an animal he could not name, with a long tail, like a fox. When he tried to catch the animal by the tail, it always went the opposite way from where he was reaching, showing its teeth, as if it were laughing. The wise man wrote down his dream. He thought it meant that although truth may be within reach, we never know all the facts.

13 The Farmer and the Ape

Krylov

One man was seen as the best farmer in the whole land. Hoeing, ploughing, planting... nobody could beat him.

Now this man had an ape who wanted to be as famous as his master. All day and every day, he was busy hoeing, muck-spreading, ploughing and planting, rolling barrels... but it was no good. The only work which got any praise was the work done by the man.

14 The Clever Tortoise

The Amazon

A man was going along when he saw a tortoise playing a flute! "What lovely music!" he cried, taking both tortoise and flute home in a box!

Next day, the man went to work, leaving his three children to look after the clever tortoise. When the tortoise began playing the flute, the children went to the box to listen to him, and he heard them talking.

"You like my music?" he cried. "You should see me dance!"

The children opened the box and the tortoise came out and began dancing all around the room. Suddenly, he stopped.

"I need some air!" he cried. "Can I step outside?"

"Yes, of course!" said one. "I'll open the door!" smiled the second.

"Take care!" added the third.

Well, the tortoise went out, straight down the path – and all the way home, where he is probably still playing his flute to this day!

15 The Dishonest Porcupine

from Africa

A man borrowed an ivory comb from his neighbour. He was going to a wedding and wanted to look special.

When his neighbour went to ask for it back – the man said he had never borrowed it!

But, as he spoke, the teeth of the ivory comb sprung out all over his body, to show how untruthful he was. And that man became – the porcupine!

16 The Cat and the Mice

de la Fontaine

A cat was such a good mouser that the mice had to think of some way to stop him. "Let us put a bell on the cat's collar," said one. "Then we shall hear him coming!"

But there was nobody who dared put the bell on the cat's collar.

There is never a shortage of those who will speak. But those who put words into actions are always much fewer.

17 The Ox of Straw

from the Ukraine

A man and his wife were trying to think of ways to make a living. One day, as they looked around, the wife said, "Can you make me an ox out of straw? I have an idea!" So the man made an ox of straw, which the wife covered with tar. Then they put it in the field, and hid. Soon, an old bear with bare patches on its fur went up to it. "Who are you?" he said.

"An ox of straw spread with tar!" came the man's voice.

"I need straw and tar to patch up a few places!" said the bear.

"Take as much as you like!" came the reply. But as soon as the bear bit the straw, he found himself stuck, then chained up!

"Let me go!" he cried. "You can have all the honey you want!" The man unchained the bear, and got enough honey to open a sweet factory! How lucky the wife had seen that old bear! How important it is to keep your eyes open!

18 The Mermaid and the Fisherman

Melegari

A young girl loved a fisherman and dreamed of being his wife. But he had a sweetheart. And when she saw them in his boat, she knew her dream was false.

She jumped into the water, following the boat. All at once, a feeling of great cold rose up from her feet to her waist, and a voice called to her from the bottom of the sea. Down she went, and became – a mermaid!

19 The Daredevil Donkey

from Arabia

A man was leading his donkey along by its halter, unaware that two thieves were watching. "I'll get the donkey," said one. "You take it to market!" The thief crept up and gently pulled the donkey's head from the halter. Then as his friend took the animal, he put the halter over his own neck and walked behind the owner. When the donkey and his friend were out of sight, he stopped, and the man turned around.

"Who are you?" he cried.

"Your donkey!" said the thief. "When I was a boy, I played a trick on a magician and he turned me into a donkey for seven years, seven days and seven hours! Now, the spell is broken!"

"How sad!" sighed the man. He let the thief go, then went to market to buy another donkey.

That was when he saw his own donkey! "Played another trick on a magician already, have you?" he said in its ear. "I'm not buying YOU again!"

20 The Advice of Three Monkeys

from Japan

There was once a man who kept three very clever monkeys.

One day, he was at the window when he saw a big car crash into a street lamp, mount the pavement and knock over a greengrocer's barrow, then speed away as if nothing had happened! But the man had got the number of the car!

"I must telephone the police!" he told the three monkeys. "Or the hospital first, do you think? The greengrocer might be hurt! Or, what about an ambulance? What shall I do?" The first monkey put his hands over his eyes.

"Right!" said the man. "I say that I saw nothing!" He passed to the second monkey, who had his hands over his ears. "So!" cried the man. "I heard nothing, either!" The third monkey was ready with his hands over his mouth.

"What's that?" cried the man. "I must not speak? So how can I say that I heard nothing and saw nothing?"

21 The Cockerel and the crumbs

Brothers Grimm

A cockerel saw the farmer going out after lunch. "Let us find some left-overs!" he said to the hen. "The farmer's wife has not cleared the table!"

"We are not allowed inside the house!" said the hen.

"But think what lovely food there is on the tablecloth!" said Cockerel.

"Think what a lovely beating we'll get if we're caught!" Hen pointed out.

"Come on!" said Cockerel. "You can have first choice!"

They were pecking crumbs from the tablecloth, when in came the farmer's wife, hitting them with a broom! The cockerel fluttered about, dodging many blows. The hen was hit on her crest, her back and her tail.

And when they were back in the farmyard, the cockerel turned to the hen and said, "Don't ever let me hear you say that you want crumbs from the table again! Silly hen!"

22 The Chimpanzee who needed spectacles

Krylov

When an old chimpanzee mistook his grandson for a gorilla, he knew he needed spectacles.

His son had worked in a circus. So he had got to know the ways of humans and told his father of shops which sold spectacles to help poor sight. So the chimpanzee went into town with his grandson and found a shop with lots of spectacles on display!

The chimpanzee took a pair and put them on one shoulder. His grandson still looked like a gorilla. He took another pair and put them on his other shoulder. There was no change. "You put spectacles over the EYES!" the man in the shop managed to say at last.

So the chimpanzee put them over the eyes of his grandson. And what a fright he got! Now his grandson looked human!

"Are you trying to make a monkey out of me?" the chimpanzee roared. And he stormed towards the door – of the broom cupboard!

23 The Dog and the Porcupine

from Africa

Dogs hate porcupines as much as they hate cats! It all began when the porcupine came and asked the dog for food and a bed where he could rest his spiky back. There was no problem finding a bed – and when it came to food the dog gave the porcupine some sugar cane to try. The porcupine liked it very much!

"Good!" barked the dog. He showed the porcupine a field of sugar cane belonging to a judge. "Eat what you like!" he said. "But leave the roots, so that it will grow again!"

So the porcupine went into the field and ate not only the sugar cane, but also the roots. When the judge found out, the dog blamed the porcupine. The porcupine blamed the dog!

"Let us settle it in court!" said the porcupine, and the judge and the dog agreed.

The porcupine waited until the weather got cold. Then one morning when it was still dark and freezing cold, he went to get the dog. "Come on!" he said, the dog's teeth chattering with cold. "Let's settle this!"

The dog was still shivering when the judge appeared. "See how the dog trembles, Your Honour!" cried the porcupine. "Proof that he stole your sugar cane!"

The judge had to believe the porcupine – the dog was so cold, he could say nothing!

And that is why, when any dog sees a porcupine, it will bark without stopping!

24 The Conceited Little Donkey

Aesop

A man treated his mule and his horse in exactly the same way.

The mule began to get very vain. "My mother was a race-horse!" he kept saying. "And I can gallop as well as she could!" But he could not gallop for long, and it was then he remembered that his father was a donkey.

We have to consider both sides of any argument before making up our minds.

25 The Ox, the Ass and the Angel

Melegari

The story of the first Christmas and the Birth of the Christ Child in Bethlehem has been told many, many times over the centuries. There are also many stories telling how the ox and the ass came to see the Baby, with Mary and Joseph in the stable.

We have to remember that the nights are very cold in the part of the world where Jesus was born. And there was no way of heating a stable!

So it was the ox and ass who warmed the Christ Child with their breath. But as the night hours passed, the donkey began to feel cold and his nose began to twitch, as if he was going to sneeze.

The Christ Child began feeling cold, too. He lifted up His eyes at one of the angels who had given news of His birth to the shepherds.

The little angel bent over him and the donkey, covering them both with its wings, to warm them on that Holy Night.

26 The Lotus Flower, the Goose and the Stars

from India

The lotus is a plant with a beautiful yellow flower, like stars. It bears a fruit, too – but it is the lotus flower which contains seeds with the pleasant and strong taste of aniseed. That is why lotus plants are grown in eastern countries – and why the goose in this story went to see if she could find any! Well, that goose walked and walked, until, by nightfall, she had reached the shores of a lake, so tired that she could hardly keep her eyes open.

Then, she opened her eyes wide. "There's a lotus flower!" she cried, pecking at the lake! The reflection of the stars made it look like a field of lotus flowers!

But, after she had pecked at nothing but water, she put her head under her wing and slept. When she woke next morning, she was in a big field of lotus flowers! "It was the work of the stars!" she said, settling down for a good feed.

27 The Porcupine and the Teasel Brush

from Africa

Teasel brushes have very fine teeth. People use them to make materials velvety-smooth. Once there were so few , it seemed a thief was stealing them!

"Me?" said the thief. "Steal a teasel brush? I don't even know what it is!" But everyone knew he was untruthful, when, at that very moment, the thief became a porcupine, the only living teasel brush there is!

28 The Riddle of the Sphinx

Melegari

The sphinx was a monster with the head of a woman, the wings of a bird and a lion's body. A stone image built in ancient times still dominates the Egyptian desert.

The real sphinx lived on a rock outside Thebes in Greece. There she gave travellers a riddle. When they failed to answer it, they perished. The sphinx set a man named Oedipus the same riddle.

"Who is it who walks on four legs in the morning, two at mid-day and on three in the evening?"

"Man!" cried Oedipus. "In the morning of his life, that is the first months, man crawls on all fours. As an adult, that is at mid-day, he walks on two legs. And when he is old – that is to say, by evening – he helps his two legs with a third, a walking stick!"

The sphinx could not bear the shame of being beaten. She threw herself off the cliff where she had lain in wait for victims and became a legend.

29 The Broom and the Spider

Melegari

Do you know why a broom stays in a corner? Because it cannot make friends!

"The broom is my enemy!" says the spider.

"It is not my fault," the broom answers, "if people use me to brush down your web! It's your fault for putting them where they should not be!"

From the most humble, there is always something to learn.

30 The Flying Fish and the Gull

Aesop

Flying fish feed on things in the sea. They also leap out and fly. Gulls fly and eat things in the sea, too. But they have their nests on the ground! When a gull swallowed a sea-urchin, it was so painful! "If you eat sea food," said a wise flying fish, "you have to know what is in the sea!"

We must always prepare for a difficult task. Then we shall be taking no risks.

31 The Lazy Little Seal

Melegari

There was a baby seal at the zoo! But he was the despair of his mother. He did not want to learn how to balance a ball on its nose, to play a tune on old car horns, or sit up on his flippers. He just liked being lazy and doing nothing.

In the end, his trainer built a pen away from the other animals. "You can stay there," said the man, "until you learn how to behave!" Now, the little seal knew that things were serious. He began feeling sorry that he had been so lazy.

He was wondering what he could do, along came a boy who was going to a show at the zoo. "Hey!" he cried, coming up to the little seal. "I've told my friend at school that you can do tricks with a ball without dropping it once! Can you show me how it's done?"

He took a beach ball from his pocket and blew it up. Then he threw it to the seal.

The little seal caught it on his nose, tossed it up, let it fall on his chest, threw it up again, then caught it on one flipper, then on the other, then tossed the ball up again!

By this time a crowd had gathered round. They began to laugh, then to clap, then to cheer. And when the seal saw the Director of the Zoo with a big smile on his face, he knew he was the star of the show! Much better, he decided, than being lazy and doing nothing!

Or – was it that he found learning easier when he was working with someone he liked?

Index

Index

Index

Index